Metaphysical Foundations of Natural Science

The Library of Liberal Arts

IMMANUEL
KANT

Metaphysical Foundations of Natural Science

Translated, with Introduction
and Essay, by

JAMES ELLINGTON

The University of Connecticut

The Library of Liberal Arts
published by
THE BOBBS-MERRILL COMPANY, INC.
Indianapolis and New York

IMMANUEL KANT
1724–1804
Die metaphysischen Anfangsgründe der Naturwissenschaft
was originally published in 1786

TRANSLATOR'S PREFACE

The only English translation of Kant's *Metaphysical Foundations of Natural Science* made before the present one is that by Ernest Belfort Bax, first published in Bohn's Philosophical Library at London in 1883, and now out of print for many years. In Bax's "Preface" he says that "in the *Anfangsgründe* Kant seems to have surpassed himself in clumsiness and obscurity of style. In several sentences the verb is wanting, and others by the omission of a negative particle or a similar carelessness, make precisely the reverse sense of that, judging by the context, obviously intended." With the best intentions in the world Bax struggled valiantly with Kant's clumsy sentences, but often missed the meaning intended. His translation is very literal, and because of the unusual word order, often makes the English reader feel uncomfortable. I have tried to profit by Bax's mistakes. I have always aimed at rendering Kant's meaning in readable sentences. But the difficulties involved in trying to realize this aim are formidable; I sympathize with Bax in his complaints about the many obscurities of the German text.

The *Metaphysical Foundations of Natural Science* was published in 1786. Many books and articles have been written about this work; an impressive list of them can be found at the end of Buek's "Introduction" to the Philosophische Bibliothek edition of the *Metaphysical Foundations*. Most of them are in German. Up till now this important work of Kant has not been widely read and studied in the English world.

I want to express my gratitude to Wolfgang Paulsen of the University of Massachusetts for helping me disentangle some of the knottiest sentences of the German text. Walter Watson of the State University of New York at Stony Brook provided invaluable aid in some of the technical scientific passages of the text. Warner Wick of the University of Chicago provided unfailing help in all stages and aspects of my work.

JAMES ELLINGTON

The University of Connecticut
October 1968

CONTENTS

TRANSLATOR'S INTRODUCTION

The *Metaphysical Foundations of Natural Science* is a neglected work. This is unfortunate, because it tells us many interesting things and has an important function in the overall structure of Kant's philosophy of physical science. Many people seem to think that mining the "Transcendental Analytic" of the *Critique of Pure Reason* is the most profitable venture for learning what Kant thinks about the philosophical presuppositions of physics (perhaps mainly, or at least in part, because no accurate English translation of the *Metaphysical Foundations* has been available). It is quite true that the "Transcendental Analytic" contains his most general thoughts on the subject, but the *Metaphysical Foundations* is an indispensable stage in the passage from the highly abstract transcendental discussions of the "Analytic" to the more concrete treatment of nature in empirical physics.

In this carefully structured philosophical system of corporeal nature, the *Metaphysical Foundations* fits in between the "Analytic" and the *Transition from the Metaphysical Foundations of Natural Science to Physics*. Most people are even less familiar with this latter work than with the *Metaphysical Foundations*. The *Transition* is unfinished, making up a part of a project which Kant was working on at the time of his death (see below, page 214), and which survived as a stack of handwritten sheets. Editors later gathered these into thirteen fascicles, collectively called the *Opus Postumum*, to be found in Volumes XXI and XXII of the Royal Prussian Academy of Sciences edition of Kant's writings. The relationship among these three works is a hierarchical one. The overall organization of the *Metaphysical Foundations* depends upon a schema developed in the *Critique*. And, as one might expect, there are frequent references in the former to the latter (see below, pages, 6, 11, 15–16, 102, 104–105, 106–107, 118–120, for example). Therefore, some familiarity with the "Analytic" is necessary if one is to understand the *Metaphysical Foundations*. The *Transition*, in turn, depends on the *Metaphysical Foundations*. The essay at the end of this translation is intended for those who are interested in the definitive architectonic interconnections among the *Critique,* the *Metaphysical Foundations,* and the *Transition.*

Here in the Introduction our aim is not so ambitious. In order to get some idea of the architectonic relations involved, let us consider an example. When a rock is thrown in a direction parallel to the ground, we know by experience that its path is a curvilinear line ending on the ground some yards away; how many yards away depends on how strong the pitcher is. The exact nature of the curvilinear path depends upon the mass of the rock, the velocity it attains by means of the force the pitcher imparts when he throws it, the resistance of the air through which it passes, and the pull of gravity upon it. When these things are known, we can plot the exact path by the laws of physics, which are generalizations from many experiments. But we are also told that if the air exerted no resistance and if gravity exerted no pull, then the rock would keep on going forever in a straight line (provided no hills got in the way before it cleared the planet earth and no celestial objects blocked its path after it left the earth). This is Newton's first law of motion, which says that every object continues in a state of rest or of uniform motion (constant velocity or zero acceleration) in a straight line unless acted upon by some outside force—a curious law that would seem to hold for some science-fiction world rather than our own. In our world the atmosphere always offers some resistance and gravity always pulls, with the result that any rocks we ever throw always come to earth. Thus Newton's law seems to be of a character different from that of the aforementioned laws determining the paths of projectiles. Furthermore, there are philosophers who tell us that every change has a cause. This law is even more general than Newton's first law of motion, for this one covers not only the case of material bodies that stay put or else keep going in a straight line with uniform velocity unless some external cause acts upon them, but also the case of living things that act according to an internal cause (a lion rushes after an antelope not because a big puff of wind propels him but because he has a desire to eat).

Kant carefully distinguished these three different kinds of laws. Laws of the first kind are the empirical ones of physics, which are validated by experiment. The second he called metaphysical; the third transcendental. These last two kinds are not established by experience. Metaphysical and transcendental principles require a priori, philosophical justifications showing how it is that principles which in their origin owe nothing to experience are nevertheless applicable to experience. For example, according to the transcendental principle of efficient causation, all things change in conformity with the law of the connection of cause and effect. Take the case of a warm room and a glowing stove. I come out of the cold into a warm room; I feel the warmth and later notice a glowing stove. But I do not say that the warm room is the cause of the glowing stove; rather, the other way around. When we are confronted with certain successions of events, we rework the subjective order of our perceiving these events in accordance with the principle of causation and set up an objective order of the events—the stove causes the room to be warm. This universal law of efficient causation is imposed a priori upon objects by the mind itself. The various a priori forms of thought according to which we order our perceptions are explored by Kant in the *Critique of Pure Reason*, where he explains how they, though not having their origin in experience, are yet the very conditions that make experience possible as an objective synthesis of subjective sense impressions.

These metaphysical and transcendental principles are a priori in the strict sense. They are not only prior to experience, but are independent of experience in the sense that they are the necessary grounds which make experience itself possible; they have their origin in the very nature of the thinking faculty itself. One sometimes hears that hypotheses are a priori in the sense that they are prior to the experience that confirms or rejects them; however, these are not independent of experience, because all sorts of analogies, knowledge of other physical laws, educated guesses, and even plain hunches go into their manufacture. For instance, when Copernicus first thought that the planets might be moving about the sun instead of the sun and other planets moving about the earth, he was advancing a hypothesis which later proved to be a confirmable description of the solar system; but this hypothesis was a priori only in a weak sense. Kant would say that such specific hypotheses are *regulative* principles that guide empirical enquiry, but that the aforementioned strictly a priori principles are *constitutive* of experience.

What, now, are these various transcendental and metaphysical principles? Let us take up the transcendental ones first.

In the *Critique* Kant treats of the most formal functions of thought. Representations, or what a philosopher such as Locke would call ideas, are combined in consciousness (the transcendental unity of apperception) to give us objectively valid knowledge of things, e.g., the earth is a rotating body. The fundamental ways in which thoughts are so combined comprise the logical functions of judgment. These are the familiar universal, particular, singular, affirmative, negative, etc. to be found in the *Critique* (at B 95). When these twelve logical forms of judgment are employed so as to constitute the knowledge of some object, they function as categories and not simply as logical forms of thought in general. The following example points up the difference between a category and a logical function of judgment: according to the categorical form of judgment I can say that "all bodies are divisible", but I can also say that "something divisible is a body"; however, when the concept of body is subsumed under the category of substance, the empirical intuition of body must always be considered as subject and never as predicate. Similarly, the other categories are used to determine the empirical knowledge of some object.

The laws according to which the categories must apply to all objects of experience are called the principles of pure understanding (Grundsätze des reinen Verstandes). Following the order of the categories, these transcendental principles comprise a system. The **Axioms of Intuition** tell us that the intuitions of phenomena are extensive magnitudes; this means that objects are spread out in space and last through time. The **Anticipations of Perception** tell us that objects also have intensive magnitude. Since the sensible perception of objects always involves sensation (as well as the temporal and spatial intuitions treated in the Axioms), and sensation has a degree starting from the complete absence of any sensation (pure intuition) and proceeding to sensations of indefinitely increasing intensity, given through sense perception; a corresponding intensive magnitude must be ascribed to objects. And so even though all sensations as such are given only a posteriori, the fact that they have a degree can be known a priori. Accordingly color, sound, taste, and even resistance and weight must have intensive magnitude. These Axioms and Anticipations are concerned with homogeneous elements of experience which do not necessarily belong to one another; the following **Analogies of Experience** are concerned with relations of heterogeneous elements which do necessarily belong to one another. The First Analogy of Experience tells us that substance is the permanent substratum underlying all change; in every alteration there is an exchange of one state of a thing for another state of that thing, but the thing itself must remain the same. According to the Second Analogy all changes of phenomena take place in conformity with the law of the connection of cause and effect. The Third Analogy tells us that substances stand in a relation of reciprocal causality regarding their accidents. The **Postulates of Empirical Thought** are not concerned with the necessary traits of objects (as are the Axioms, Anticipations, and Analogies), but, rather, with the existence of objects in relation to the mind that knows them. The First Postulate says that if things are to be *possible,* then the concept of these things must agree with the formal conditions of experience, i.e., with the forms of intuition (time and space) and with the forms of thought that together constitute the transcendental unity of apperception. The Second Postulate tells us that what is connected with that which is given in sensation is *actual;* this means that we must have sense perception of things in order to know their actuality. The Third Postulate says that the *necessary* is that whose connection with the actual is determined according to the Analogies. The necessity here applies only to the changing states of substances and not to the substances themselves, since substances do not come to be and pass away. If we have actual experience of the cause of something, then by thought we can affirm the necessary existence of the effect.

Obviously the *Critique* treats only of the most general aspects of things. For example, through the category of substance I think of an unchanging subject to which changing predicates belong. Now, if this category is not to remain a mere abstract form of thought, there must be something permanent presented in experience corresponding to this formal concept of substance. The experience of bodies in space, with their changing characteristics, is the content that gives this abstract concept meaning and truth. In other words, the transcendental concepts and principles treated in the *Critique* must be applied to our experience of bodies (matter) if they are not to remain mere abstractions.

Now, this is one of the jobs of the *Metaphysical Founda-*

tions of Natural Science; it outlines the general ways in which the categories can be applied to matter. Matter affects the external senses (and hence becomes an object of experience) only through its motion. Consequently, the metaphysics of corporeal nature is concerned with the motion of matter. But empirical physics is concerned with this also. How do the two differ? Metaphysics is concerned with the range of the possible motions of any matter (i.e., of matter in general); physics is concerned with the actual motion of particular matter (e.g., the paths of projectiles). Even though metaphysics treats of concepts that can only be given empirically (matter and motion), it is nonetheless an a priori science, because it determines matter by means of the formal categories (as we shall soon see) instead of by empirically given predicates as does physics. If I may cite our earlier example, according to Kant's second law of mechanics (see below, p. 104), every body remains motionless or else moves with uniform velocity in a straight line as long as no external cause changes its condition of rest or uniform motion. On the other hand, a rock thrown in a line initially parallel to the ground actually describes an arc, which is determinable once we know the force with which it was thrown, the resistance of the air, and the pull of gravity on it; all of these variables are ascertained by empirical measurement.

There are, then, some things (possibilities) that we can know about objects of experience without regard to their particular traits (actualities), which are treated in physics. The *Critique* and the *Metaphysical Foundations* are both concerned with these possible characteristics of phenomenal objects, but in different degrees. The transcendental concept of substance is one of an unchanging subject to which changing predicates belong; this is the most general notion that we can have of a phenomenal object. The metaphysical concept of matter narrows this notion down; substance is determined by the possible spatial perception of matter. In other words, the metaphysical concept of matter introduces a sensible content (or "intuition" in Kant's terminology). Intuition is either empirical or pure. Through empirical intuition the physicist knows about the *actual* behavior of some definite matter (the path of a thrown rock). The metaphysician knows about the *possible* behavior (motion) of matter in general through mathematical construction (pure intuition). The mathematical constructions Kant deals with are mainly geometrical constructions in Euclidean space; for example, when two motions of one material body that is taken as a mathematical point are represented by two lines, each of which expresses velocity and direction and such that the two lines enclose an angle, then the composite motion of the point can be represented by the diagonal (expressing velocity and direction) of the parallelogram produced by drawing lines parallel to the original two lines. (Please notice that this law does not tell us what the lengths of the sides of the parallelogram will be or what the angle between the sides will be; only experience can do that in a particular case under consideration. This law is a rule for generating infinitely many cases involving all manner of angles between the lines and all lengths of the lines.)

The metaphysics of corporeal nature, then, deals with the principles of the application of transcendental concepts to matter and with the principles of the mathematical construction of such concepts as belong to the possibility of matter in general. These metaphysical principles constitute a complete system when the empirically given concept of matter is determined by the categories. These principles do not enable us to foretell or predetermine what concrete facts will be given us by experience; but they should enable us to know in a necessary way the general aspects of every possible object of physics until experience gives us the actual presence of some of these material objects, and they should guide us in formulating the questions which we devise experiments to answer.

These metaphysical principles fall into four groups cor-

responding to the categorical heads: quantity, quality, relation, and modality. I shall not list them in detail but merely
indicate the general aspects of matter they deal with. In
Phoronomy only motion is treated. Here movability in space
is the only property attributed to matter; accordingly, matter is regarded as a mathematical point. Motion is considered
as a quantum measured by velocity and direction. In **Dynamics** matter is regarded as the movable insofar as it fills a
space. Matter does so by means of a special moving force—
through the force of repulsion one body resists the approach
of another. But if this force were not balanced by any other
force, matter would disperse itself to infinity. The force of
attraction counteracts repulsion. The attractive force depends on the mass of the matter in a given space; the repulsive force rests on the degree to which the space is filled,
and this degree can be specifically very different. Consider,
for instance, a given quantity of air in a given volume. Its
attraction depends on its mass and is constant, yet it manifests more or less elasticity according to its greater or lesser
heating. And so a spectrum of material samples all with the
same mass (and hence with the same attraction) can vary
widely in repulsion running, for instance, from the density
of platinum to the rarity of helium. Therefore every space can
be thought of both as full and yet as filled in varying degrees.
In **Mechanics** bodies already in motion are regarded as
possessing moving forces (repulsive or attractive) in order
actively to impart their motions to other bodies. The three
mechanical laws state that, first, in all changes of corporeal
nature the quantity of matter taken as a whole remains the
same, unincreased and undiminished; secondly, every
change of matter has an external cause; and, thirdly, in all
communication of motion, action and reaction are always
equal to one another. **Phenomenology** is concerned with the
way in which the subject's private experience of motion can
become public experience of it. The subject's private experience of something movable becomes public when this mov-

and the *Transition* to those aspects which are less formal. After this would come physics, which is an empirical science and not an a priori, philosophical one at all.

Since the categories specify the a priori functions of the understanding completely (as I shall show in the essay), these philosophical sciences are complete systems inasmuch as these categories determine phenomenal objects in general in the *Critique,* and matter in general in the *Metaphysical Foundations,* as we have already seen. Empirical physics can never be complete: nature's secrets are inexhaustible in that the multitude of natural objects and their discoverable features are endless (see below, p. 11). (In this respect Kant differs sharply from certain other dealers in the a priori who thought that the whole of physics could be completely and exhaustively spun out of the mind itself—Schelling, for example.) Neither can a system of the mathematical principles of corporeal nature attain completeness, even though these principles are a priori. The reason is similar to that which makes completeness unattainable in empirical physics: any mathematical science involves an endless multiplicity of possible pure intuitions.

Kant stresses that any such mathematical system of corporeal nature depends on the metaphysical system (see below, pp. 9–10, 15, 16–17). The principles of the latter system indicate (among other things) what mathematical constructions are appropriate and useful for application to natural phenomena. Kant gives several examples (see pp. 25–27, 35–38, 49–56, 70–76), only one of which I shall mention here (see pp. 70–71). Consider a force that diffuses itself through space in order to act on a distant body. How is one to represent this diffusion? One common way, borrowed from optics, is to let rays diverge from a central point (the location of the force) so that an infinite number of concentric spherical surfaces are indicated thereby. Kant considers this a bad representation because the lines so drawn can never fill the space they pass through nor the spherical surface they reach, because of their divergence. A much better way is suggested by the diffusion of the illumination of a light. This illumination diffuses itself in spherical surfaces that ever increase with the square of the distance from the source. Any one of these infinitely larger spheres is uniformly illuminated, while the degree of illumination of any one of them is inversely proportional to its distance from the light source. Accordingly, a force diffuses itself uniformly throughout space, and the degree of its action on a distant body is inversely proportional to the spatial distance through which it has had to diffuse itself in order to act on this distant body. Thus a philosophical consideration of the nature of diffusing forces indicates the appropriate mathematical construction. And so the principles of the *Metaphysical Foundations* make possible a subsequent system of the mathematical principles of corporeal nature. It is not the business of metaphysics to discover applications of mathematics to phenomena (mathematical physics does that), but, rather, to pass judgment upon the legitimacy and propriety of such application.

Kant says (by implication) that in a system such as Newton's *Mathematical Principles of Natural Philosophy,* the various kinds of principles (transcendental, metaphysical, mathematical, and physical) are intermixed. Kant has sorted them out in separate systems in order to show what are the limitations of each kind and what are the errors that might arise in their use when one confuses these various kinds of principles (see below, p. 10). He claims that all natural philosophers have made use of metaphysical concepts and principles (including—probably in a distorted way—those of the *Critique* and the *Metaphysical Foundations*), even though many have disclaimed having anything to do with them (see pp. 9–10).

In general, the empiricists have denied that there are any a priori concepts or innate ideas and have taken a dim view of metaphysics, even considering it an occult science like astrology or alchemy. Newton is a good example. In the General

Scholium of the Third Book of the *Principia* he says that he has not been able to discover the cause or causes of gravity, but that he will not frame any hypotheses (whether metaphysical or physical, whether of occult qualities or mechanical) as to what these causes might be; he is opposed to inventing causes arbitrarily and employing concepts that can not be tested in experience. In his experimental philosophy, particular propositions are inferred from phenomena and later made general by induction. Kant, of course, would agree heartily with Newton on these points; but he would go on to say that there is a legitimate metaphysics, which is the necessary precondition of all experimental science.

Empiricists and rationalists always have had—and still do have—a most difficult time understanding one another. Newton would say that he wants no truck with a metaphysics that invents causes at will and that dallies with such notions as those of occult qualities (opium puts a person to sleep because it has a soporific quality). Kant would applaud this and claim that one of his own great achievements was to expose such bastard metaphysics. If Newton had understood by "metaphysics" the legitimate metaphysics (including both the transcendental system of the *Critique* and the metaphysical system of the *Metaphysical Foundations* and the *Transition*) that Kant so carefully set up, then perhaps Newton would have been more tolerant of metaphysics. In fact, Kant claims not only that Newton could not dispense with metaphysical concepts, but also that he even adopted some unfortunate ones. By what sense experience, for instance, can a person know about absolute space, absolute time, absolute motion, and indivisible, impenetrable atoms, Kant would ask. And many critics since Kant's time have raised similar objections to these most important of Newton's concepts.

Some of the most passionately worded passages in the *Metaphysical Foundations* are to be found in the "Dynamics" when Kant rails against such atomists as Democritus, Descartes, and Newton (see pp. 77–80, 90–94). According to the mechanical mode of explication of the atomists, the specific varieties of matter can be accounted for by assuming the existence of basic particles that are absolutely impenetrable, that are absolutely homogeneous (the particles differing from one another only in their shapes), and that cohere in such a fashion that their cohesion is absolutely unconquerable; and by assuming the existence of absolutely empty space. To be sure, this mechanical view of the world lends itself admirably to the elaboration of a great many mathematical laws that are experimentally verifiable. However, this mathematico-mechanical mode of explaining the specific varieties of matter pays dearly for its successes. It claims that absolutely impenetrable atoms move about in absolutely empty space, but the existence of such atoms or of such space can never be established by any experience. Furthermore, the forces causing the atoms to move through empty space must be superimposed on matter externally. Where do the forces come from, how do they make the atoms move, etc.?

As we have already seen (p. xvii), matter for Kant involves a balance of the forces of repulsion and attraction. Repulsion is thought immediately in the concept of matter, while attraction is attributed to it by inference. Through sensation repulsion makes us aware of the size, shape, and location of an extended spatial object. However, attraction by itself can give us no determinate sensible object; attraction reveals nothing but the endeavor of our body to approach a point outside us (the center of the attracting body). If matter were endowed with repulsion only, then it would disperse itself to infinity. If attraction were not balanced by repulsion, matter would coalesce in a mathematical point, and space would be empty. One force cannot be separated from the other in the concept of matter. And so both forces can be counted among things that admit of being experienced.

On the other hand, the atomist's absolute impenetrability

and absolutely empty space (like immortality and God) are not objects of any possible experience. Kant offers his meta-physico-dynamical position as a viable alternative to the mathematico-mechanical by making three substitutions. First, repulsive force (i.e., relative impenetrability having a degree determinable by experience) takes the place of the atomist's absolute impenetrability. Second, true action at a distance (attraction) takes the place of apparent action at a distance, which is supposed to operate by means of the re-pulsive forces of pressure and impact (both stemming from the impenetrability of the atoms) to produce the endeavor to approach. The usual objection to immediate (true) action at a distance is that a body cannot act where it is not. The earth can be shown experimentally to attract the moon through space that may be regarded as entirely empty; for even though matter may lie between these two bodies, this fact does not affect the attraction. And so attraction acts di-rectly in a place where it is not. Some physicists (though not Newton) have thought this a contradictory notion and have tried to reduce all attractive force to repulsive force in con-tact. Kant argues (see below, pp. 61–66) that contact is the reciprocal action of impenetrability (repulsion), which im-pedes all motion. Consequently, there must be some imme-diate attraction outside of contact and hence at a distance. The true attraction is that which occurs without the inter-vention of repulsive forces. Apparent attraction is that which operates through the repulsive forces of pressure and impact to produce the endeavor to approach. But since pressure and impact act in the opposite direction to attraction, they would have no cause lying originally in the nature of matter unless matter also possessed a fundamental force of attraction (and not one derivative from repulsion). And so even apparent at-traction must ultimately have a true one at its basis, because matter, whose pressure or impact is to be of use instead of attraction, would not even be matter if there were no true attractive forces (i.e., without the counteraction of attraction, of the ether to serve as a more acceptable alternative to the empty spaces posited by atomism. However in the *Transition* he was not so hypothetical. There he attempted to prove the existence of the ether by basing his proof upon the unity of experience. The form of all experience is space, and this is unitary; therefore experience is unitary. Now, experience is a system comprising a manifold of perceptions that are synthesized in space by the understanding. These perceptions are caused by the actions of the material forces which fill space. And so the forces of matter must collectively admit of constituting a system that conforms to the unity of possible experience. Such a system is possible only if one admits the existence of an ether having the properties listed above as the foundation of these forces. Therefore, the unity of experience requires as its a priori condition the existence of the ether. In other words, pure thought is able to certify a real existence.

This is the sort of proof one might expect from some of Kant's idealist successors instead of from the man who took such great pains to make metaphysics legitimate. However, one must remember that the *Transition* is an unfinished work. Perhaps parts of it should be attributed to senility. At any rate, the existence of the ether could cause Kant as much embarrassment as the existence of absolutely hard atoms, rattling around in empty space, could cause the atomists. He might have redefined his ether in such a way that it might have had the sort of unifying function for the domain of forces that Einstein's unified field theory is supposed to have for the gravitational and electromagnetic fields (I say "supposed to have" because not all physicists are convinced that Einstein actually succeeded in unifying the two fields).

Enough has been said about the atoms. A bit more might be said about absolute space. According to Kant absolute space is merely an idea (see pp. 20, 125–127). It is simply that space to which the motion of any empirical space can be referred. To identify such an ideal absolute space with an alleged actual empty space goes beyond the limits of all experience. Absolute motion fares no better. Absolute motion is that motion of a body which belongs to it without relation to any other body. The only possible absolute motion would, then, be the rectilinear motion of the universe; and we have no reason to assume any such rectilinear motion (see p. 131).

Obviously Newton and others could not avoid what Kant calls metaphysical notions (the most general concepts of matter, motion, space, time, force, etc.). Newton rarely uses the word "metaphysics", because it means to him what "illegitimate metaphysics" means to Kant. He speaks instead about natural philosophy (*philosophia naturalis*), and parts of this would have much the same relationship to empirical physics as has Kant's own legitimate metaphysics. However, from Kant's point of view, most of the key concepts of Newton's *philosophia naturalis* are examples of bad metaphysics —yes, illegitimate metaphysics—because they cannot be verified by any experience. Kant even calls absolute impenetrability an occult quality (*qualitas occulta;* see below, p. 48).

In the late nineteenth and early twentieth centuries physicists abandoned absolute space, absolute time, and absolute motion when relativity theory was developed; and the indivisible atom was irrevocably abandoned for a divisible one when atomic physics burgeoned in the nineteenth century. The mathematico-mechanical Newtonian concepts that had led to such fruitful work in the eighteenth and early nineteenth centuries no longer paid off handsome dividends in scientific inquiry. I do not intend for the reader to conclude from this that Newton was wrong and Kant was right. The "incomparable Mr. Newton" (to use Locke's famous epithet) will always rank as one of the world's greatest natural philosophers. But Kant, also, was a great natural philosopher, though his metaphysico-dynamical line of thought was not the fashionable one pursued by the great majority of physicists in the eighteenth and nineteenth centuries. I am not claiming, either, that Kant finally came into his own in the twentieth century. From the vantage point of contemporary science many of the notions found in the philosophies of both Newton and Kant seem antiquated. I do claim that the lines of thought both men championed have had their adherents down through the years, and that those lines of thought are still recognizable in today's philosophic and scientific discussions. In the nineteenth century William Whewell gained much inspiration from Kant's philosophy; in the twentieth century Ernst Cassirer drew on it.

What do scientists today think about the nature of matter—a question that intrigued Kant so much? Modern atomic theory began in the last half of the nineteenth century. By the early twentieth century the Rutherford-Bohr atomic model replaced the indivisible, impenetrable atom of Democritus, Galileo, or Newton. This new model represents the atom as a miniature solar system comprising a central positive electrical charge called the nucleus, around which negatively charged electrons move. The main mass of the atom is concentrated in the nucleus; this is composed of protons each having a positive charge and neutrons having no charge. An atom of oxygen, for instance, has a nucleus containing eight protons and eight neutrons; eight electrons move about the nucleus in two shells, two electrons moving in the inner shell and six in the outer. This analysis of the atom is the first depth to which the modern treatment of matter has penetrated; it is the domain of atomic physics, which is concerned with the atom as a whole—how a positively charged nucleus holds a family of negatively charged electrons in its vicinity. The laws of atomic physics explain chemical reactions and the physical behavior of matter in either non-living or living things.

The next level of analysis is the study of the structure of the nucleus itself—nuclear physics. Like the atom itself, the nucleus is composed of concentric shells each of which can

comfortably hold only a limited number of protons and neutrons; but the shells here are much closer together than the
atomic shells. When the nucleus breaks up, great quantities
of energy are released. This splitting of the nucleus is what
produces the atomic bomb and is what releases the energy
of the stars. The various forms of stellar combustion fuse
hydrogen to produce helium, "burn" helium to make carbon, and transform carbon into oxygen. Nuclear physics also
explains the processes of radioactivity, i.e., why it is that some
clusters of protons and neutrons are stable and why others
live for only a limited time.

The third level of analysis centers on the components of
the nucleus. Are protons and neutrons "elementary," or are
they formed from even smaller basic units called quarks? This
is the domain of particle physics. If there is such a particle
as the quark, then it is the simplest in the universe and that
out of which almost everything else is made. The various
components of the nucleus were found to be far more manifold than the protons and neutrons of the original Rutherford-Bohr atomic model. By 1962 almost one hundred different kinds of particles had been observed emerging from
the nucleus—not only protons and neutrons, but such items
as positrons, electrons, muons, neutrinos, pions, photons,
etc. The quark is the basic hypothetical entity that is supposed to bring order into this confusing picture—all the particles that have so far been identified may be composed of
quarks.

The atomistic procedure involved here is much more elaborate and elegant than anything Newton could have dreamed
of. He explained the varieties of matter by assuming the
existence of basic particles that were alike except for their
differing shapes and sizes. Thus, an oxygen atom would have
one shape and size, cobalt another. We now know that there
are over one hundred elements in the universe; Newton
would have needed over one hundred different basic atoms.
Today we think of an atom as something composed of a com-

plex nucleus with electron orbits. Now, the components of an atom may ultimately be quarks, which are all alike. And so instead of over one hundred basic building blocks of the universe, there may be only one. Democritus, Galileo, and Newton would marvel at that! Of course, the quark may turn out to be nothing but a useful mathematical figment and not a concrete building block of matter at all; in that case new theories may emerge.

Not all physicists would subscribe to this atomistic approach. Einstein has suggested that there might be special kinds of fields which have modes of motion such that there would be pulse-like concentrations of fields. These would cohere in a stable fashion and act almost exactly like small moving bodies. The so-called fundamental particles may be nothing but such modes of motion of the fields; in other words, the fields are more basic than the so-called particles. This view follows more closely the tradition of Kant and of Leibniz, who held that force is substance, than it does the aforementioned atomistic tradition. If the theory of quarks bogs down, perhaps physicists will develop Einstein's suggestions. And these two are not the only philosophic views on the nature of matter. Whitehead developed another in his process philosophy of events, and man's ingenuity has proposed even others.

If Kant were to come to life today, would the intervening developments in science force him to change his mind about the Critical Philosophy? What do mathematical logic, non-Euclidean geometry, relativity theory, and quantum mechanics do to Kant's general metaphysics (including the systems of the *Critique,* the *Metaphysical Foundations,* and the *Transition*)? More generally, what is the relationship between philosophy and the special sciences for Kant? The concepts and principles of philosophy have their origin in the very nature of the thinking faculty itself, as I shall definitively show in the essay following the translation of the *Metaphysical Foundations.* These functions of thought are independent of the accidents of psychological phenomena, and they specify the thinking faculty completely. And so the "logical" is quite different from the "psychological"—a fact which Frege understood well enough, but which many contemporary logicians do not. Logic, whether the general kind found in Kant's logical writings or the transcendental kind found in the Critiques (see pp. xii–xiv, above), can attain completeness, whereas empirical psychology never can, if for no other reason than that the multitude of psychological phenomena is endless. Now, the sciences make use of these philosophical concepts and principles because, if Kant is right, to think at all means to use these formal concepts and principles to determine an empirical content. In other words, science depends upon philosophy, but philosophy does not depend upon science. I am speaking, now, about the essential order of dependence. Euclidean geometry may have suggested to Kant certain thoughts about the formal nature of space as treated in the "Transcendental Aesthetic" of the Critique, or the physical law of the conservation of matter suggested to him the First Analogy, which deals with the permanence of substance; but these are questions of the order of discovery, not of the essential order of dependence. The doctrines of the Critique do not depend upon Aristotelian logic (though they do depend upon Kant's own theory of general logic), Euclidean geometry, and Newtonian mechanics (though many people have thought otherwise). Accordingly, non-Aristotelian logic, non-Euclidean geometry, and non-Newtonian mechanics would not of themselves force Kant to change his mind about his basic philosophical system. He might want to expand certain parts and contract others, but there would be no need for him to abandon his basic approach to metaphysics.

Philosophers who know little about science often display a childlike trust in its sanctity. They manifest a blind faith in the infallibility of relativity theory or quantum mechanics. Scientists themselves exhibit no such faith. As far back as the

1930's there were non-Einsteinian general relativity theories. Einstein developed a general relativity theory with gravitation; E. A. Milne set forth one without gravitation. So far the validity of the special theory of relativity is unquestioned, but in 1966 Professor Robert H. Dicke of Princeton challenged the correctness of Einstein's field equations in his general theory. Einstein assumed that the sun is spherical; Professor Dicke claimed that the sun is oblate (flattened at the poles), and consequently that the behavior of the orbit of Mercury's perihelion could be accounted for without recourse to relativity effects. Thus Einstein's general theory might have to be abandoned or revised. When one turns to that other pillar of modern science, quantum mechanics, he finds not only the well-known indeterministic mechanics developed by Bohr and Heisenberg, but also a lesser known, more deterministic one sought after by such luminaries as Einstein, Louis de Broglie, and David Bohm. I have already mentioned (pp. xxvii–xxix) the fervent research in nuclear physics and particle physics. However, all this richly varied scientific inquiry should not bewilder and dismay the philosopher. It simply points out the fact that the New Jerusalem is as elusive in science as it is in philosophy or religion. Let man keep thinking! That is his glory.

The problem today for Kant or for a disciple would be not so much to overhaul the Critical Philosophy in the light of modern science (assumed to be definitive) as to show how the categories are functioning or might function better in contemporary science, how a clearer understanding of them might provide viable options in present discussions, how they might help to solve problems which other philosophical theories cannot. This would be a task truly worthy of the genius of another Kant.

J. W. E.

NOTE ON THE TEXT

This translation is based on Volume Four of the Königliche Preussische Akademie der Wissenschaften edition of Kant's works (1902–1938). Page numbers in that edition, the standard reference for Kant's works, here appear as marginal numbers.

All material added by me in notes or text of the translation has been bracketed.

J. W. E.

Metaphysical Foundations of Natural Science

PREFACE

If the word "nature" is taken merely in its formal signification (inasmuch as the word "nature" signifies the primal,
internal principle of everything that belongs to the existence
of a thing[1]), then there can be as many natural sciences as
there are specifically different things, and each of these
things must contain its specific internal principle of the determinations belonging to its existence. On the other hand,
"nature" is also taken in a material signification to be not a
quality but the sum total of all things insofar as they can be
objects of our senses and hence also objects of experience,
under which is therefore to be understood the whole of all
appearances, i.e., the sense-world with the exclusion of all
objects that are not sensible. Nature taken in this signification of the word has two main parts according to the main
distinction of our senses: the one contains the objects of the
external senses, the other the object of the internal sense.
Therefore, a twofold doctrine of nature is possible: a *doctrine
of body* and a *doctrine of soul*. The first considers extended
nature, and the second, thinking nature.

Every doctrine, if it is to be a system, i.e., a whole of cognition ordered according to principles, is called science. And
since principles can be either of the empirical or of the rational connection of cognitions in a whole, so natural sci- *468*
ence, be it the doctrine of body or the doctrine of soul,
would have to be divided into historical and rational natural
science, were it not that the word "nature" (because this

---

[1] Essence is the primal, internal principle of everything that belongs to the
possibility of a thing. Therefore, one can attribute to geometrical figures only
an essence and not a nature (since there is thought in their concept nothing
which expresses an existence).

3

word designates the derivation of the manifold belonging to
the existence of things from their internal principle) neces-
sitates a rational cognition of the coherence of things, so far
as this cognition is to deserve the name of natural science.
Therefore, the doctrine of nature might better be divided
into the historical doctrine of nature, which contains nothing
but the systematically ordered facts regarding natural things
(which again would consist of the description of nature as
a system of classes of natural things ordered according to
similarities, and the history of nature as a systematic presentation of natural things in different times and in different
places), and natural science. Now, natural science would in
turn be natural science either properly or improperly so
called; the first would treat its object wholly according to a
priori principles, and the second, according to laws of experience.

Only that whose certainty is apodeictic can be called science proper; cognition that can contain merely empirical
certainty is only improperly called science. That whole of
cognition which is systematic can therefore be called science,
and, when the connection of cognition in this system is a
coherence of grounds and consequents, rational science.
But when these grounds or principles are ultimately merely
empirical, as, for example, in chemistry, and when the laws
from which reason explains the given facts are merely laws
of experience, then they carry with themselves no consciousness of their necessity (are not apodeictically certain), and
thus the whole does not in a strict sense deserve the name of
science. Therefore, chemistry should be called systematic
art rather than science.

A rational doctrine of nature, then, deserves the name of
natural science only when the natural laws that underlie it
are cognized a priori and are not mere laws of experience.
Natural cognition of the first kind is called pure, but that of
the second kind is called applied rational cognition. Since
the word "nature" already carries with it the concept of laws

and since this concept carries with it the concept of the necessity of all the determinations of a thing which belong to its existence, it is easily seen why natural science must derive *469* the legitimacy of its designation only from a pure part of natural science, namely, from that part which contains the a priori principles of all remaining natural explications, and why natural science is only by virtue of this pure part science proper. And so every doctrine of nature must according to the demands of reason ultimately aim at natural science and terminate in it, inasmuch as the necessity of laws attaches inseparably to the concept of nature and must therefore be thoroughly understood. Hence the most complete explication of certain phenomena by chemical principles always leaves dissatisfaction in its wake, inasmuch as through these contingent laws learned by mere experience no a priori grounds can be adduced.

Thus all natural science proper requires a pure part, upon which the apodeictic certainty sought by reason in such science can be based. And since this pure part is according to its principles completely different by comparison with that part whose principles are only empirical, there is the greatest advantage (indeed according to the nature of the case there is, as regards the method, an indispensable duty) in expounding this pure part separately and entirely unmixed with the empirical part and in expounding this pure part as far as possible in its completeness, in order that one may be able to determine exactly what reason can accomplish of itself and where its capacity begins to require the assistance of principles of experience. Pure rational cognition from mere concepts is called pure philosophy, or metaphysics; on the other hand, that pure rational cognition which is based only upon the construction of concepts by means of the presentation of the object in a priori intuition is called mathematics.[2]

Natural science properly so called presupposes metaphys-

[2] [Cf. *Critique of Pure Reason*, B 740–755.]

ics of nature; for laws, i.e., principles of the necessity of what belongs to the existence of a thing, are occupied with a concept which does not admit of construction, because existence cannot be presented in any a priori intuition.[3] Therefore, natural science proper presupposes metaphysics of nature. Now, the latter must indeed always contain nothing but principles which are not empirical (for that reason it bears the name of a metaphysics). But either it can treat of the laws which make possible the concept of a nature in general even without reference to any determinate object of experience, and therefore undetermined regarding the nature of this or that thing of the sense-world—and in this case it is
470   the transcendental part of the metaphysics of nature[4]—or it occupies itself with the special nature of this or that kind of things, of which an empirical concept is given in such a way that besides what lies in this concept, no other empirical principle is needed for cognizing the things. For example, it lays the empirical concept of a matter or of a thinking being at its foundation and searches the range of cognition of which reason is a priori capable regarding these objects. Such a science must still be called a metaphysics of nature, namely, of corporeal or of thinking nature; however, it is then not a general but a special metaphysical natural science (physics and psychology), in which the aforementioned transcendental principles are applied to the two species of sense-objects.

I maintain, however, that in every special doctrine of nature only so much science proper can be found as there is mathematics in it. For in accordance with the foregoing considerations, science proper, especially science of nature, requires a pure part, which lies at the foundation of the empirical part and is based upon an a priori cognition of natural things.

---

[3] [Cf. *ibid.*, B 740–755.]

[4] [This transcendental part is contained in the *Critique of Pure Reason,* B 170–294, "The Analytic of Principles" (Book II of the Transcendental Analytic).]

Now, to cognize anything a priori is to cognize it from its mere possibility. But the possibility of determinate natural things cannot be cognized from their mere concepts; from these concepts the possibility of the thought (that it does not contradict itself) can indeed be cognized, but not the possibility of the object as a natural thing, which can be given (as existing) outside of the thought. Therefore, in order to cognize the possibility of determinate natural things, and hence to cognize them a priori, there is further required that the intuition corresponding to the concept be given a priori, i.e., that the concept be constructed. Now, rational cognition through the construction of concepts is mathematical. A pure philosophy of nature in general, i.e., one that only investigates what constitutes the concept of a nature in general, may indeed be possible without mathematics; but a pure doctrine of nature concerning determinate natural things (doctrine of body and doctrine of soul) is possible only by means of mathematics. And since in every doctrine of nature only so much science proper is to be found as there is a priori cognition in it, a doctrine of nature will contain only so much science proper as there is applied mathematics in it.

So long, then, as there is for the chemical actions of matters on one another no concept which admits of being constructed, i.e., no law of the approach or withdrawal of the *471* parts of matters can be stated according to which (as, say, in proportion to their densities and suchlike) their motions together with the consequences of these can be intuited and presented a priori (a demand that will hardly ever be fulfilled), chemistry can become nothing more than a systematic art or experimental doctrine, but never science proper; for the principles of chemistry are merely empirical and admit of no presentation a priori in intuition. Consequently, the principles of chemical phenomena cannot make the possibility of such phenomena in the least conceivable inasmuch as they are incapable of the application of mathematics.[5]

But the empirical doctrine of the soul must always remain yet even further removed than chemistry from the rank of what may be called a natural science proper. This is because mathematics is inapplicable to the phenomena of the internal sense and their laws, unless one might want to take into consideration merely the law of continuity in the flow of this sense's internal changes. But the extension of cognition so attained would bear much the same relation to the extension of cognition which mathematics provides for the doctrine of body, as the doctrine of the properties of the straight line bears to the whole of geometry. The reason for the limitation on this extension of cognition lies in the fact that the pure internal intuition in which the soul's phenomena are to be constructed is time, which has only one dimension. But not even as a systematic art of analysis or as an experimental doctrine can the empirical doctrine of the soul ever approach chemistry, because in it the manifold of internal observation is separated only by mere thought, but cannot be kept separate and be connected again at will; still less does another thinking subject submit to our investigations in such a way as to be conformable to our purposes, and even the observation itself alters and distorts the state of the object observed. It can, therefore, never become anything more than a historical (and as such, as much as possible) systematic natural doctrine of the internal sense, i.e., a natural description of the soul, but not a science of the soul, nor even a psychological experimental doctrine. This is the reason why in the title of this work, which, properly speaking, contains the principles of the doctrine of body, we have employed, in accordance with the usual practice, the general name of natural science; for this designation in the strict sense belongs

---

[5] [The beginnings of the modern science of chemistry were made by Lavoisier shortly before the *Metaphysical Foundations* appeared in 1786. Kant did not foresee the development of atomic physics, which was to make chemistry a science.]

to the doctrine of body alone and hence causes no ambiguity.

But in order to make possible the application of mathe-   *472* matics to the doctrine of body, which can become natural science only by means of such application, principles of the construction of concepts that belong to the possibility of matter in general must precede. Hence a complete analysis of the concept of a matter in general must be laid at the foundation of the doctrine of body. This is the business of pure philosophy, which for this purpose makes use of no particular experiences but uses only what it finds in the separated (although in itself empirical) concept [of matter] with regard to pure intuitions in space and time (according to laws which already depend essentially on the concept of nature in general); hence such a doctrine is an actual metaphysics of corporeal nature.

All natural philosophers who wanted to proceed mathematically in their work had therefore always (though unknown to themselves) made use of metaphysical principles, and had to make use of them, even though they otherwise solemnly repudiated any claim of metaphysics on their science. Doubtless they understood by metaphysics the illusion of inventing possibilities at will and playing with concepts which perhaps do not at all admit of presentation in intuition and have no other certification of their objective reality than the fact that they merely do not stand in contradiction with themselves. All true metaphysics is taken from the essential nature of the thinking faculty itself and therefore is by no means invented. This is because metaphysics is not borrowed from experience but contains the pure operations of thought, and hence contains concepts and principles a priori, which first of all bring the manifold of empirical representations into legitimate connection, whereby such a manifold can become empirical *cognition,* i.e., experience. Those mathematical physicists could not at all, then, dispense with metaphysical principles, and among these principles, not with such as make the concept of their own special object, namely, matter, available a priori for application to external experience (as in the cases of the concept of motion, of the filling of space, of inertia, etc.). However, they rightly held that letting merely empirical principles prevail in these questions would be not at all compatible with the apodeictic certainty which they wanted to give to their natural laws; therefore, they preferred to postulate such laws without investigating their a priori sources.

473   But of the greatest importance for the benefit of the sciences is severing heterogeneous principles from one another and bringing each kind into a separate system, so that each may constitute a science of its own kind in order thereby to avoid the uncertainty which arises from confusing such heterogeneous principles; for a person cannot well distinguish to which of the two kinds of principles are to be attributed, on the one hand, the limitations, and, on the other, the errors which might occur in their use. For this reason I have deemed it necessary that from the pure part of natural science (*physica generalis*), where metaphysical and mathematical constructions are accustomed to traverse one another, the metaphysical constructions, and with them also the principles of the construction of these metaphysical concepts (and hence the principles of the possibility of a mathematical doctrine of nature itself), be presented in one system.[6] This separation, beside the aforementioned advantage which such a separation provides, has in addition a special charm afforded by the unity of knowledge when a person takes care that the boundaries of the sciences do not run into one another but occupy their properly divided fields.

There may serve as a second ground for recommending this procedure the fact that in all that is called metaphysics

[6] [Kant means that he is going to gather the metaphysical principles into one system, namely, *The Metaphysical Foundations of Natural Science;* and this system then makes possible a subsequent mathematical system of nature such as Newton's.]

more pure concepts of the understanding, which can con-
475   cern the nature of things. Under the four classes of quantity,
quality, relation, and finally modality, all determinations of
476   the universal concept of a matter in general and, therefore,
everything that can be thought a priori respecting it, that can
be presented in mathematical construction, or that can be
given in experience as a determinate object of experience,
must be capable of being brought. There is no more to do

---

apodeictic conviction requisite for compelling an unqualified acceptance. This
main foundation is said to be my deduction of the pure concepts of the
understanding, expounded partly in the *Critique* and partly in the *Prolegomena*, but which in that part of the *Critique* that should have been the clearest
is said to be the most obscure or indeed to move in a circle, etc. I direct
my answers to these objections only to their chief point, namely, that without
a completely clear and adequate deduction of the categories the system of
the *Critique of Pure Reason* would totter on its foundation. I maintain, on the
contrary, that for those who subscribe to my propositions as to the sensibility
of all our intuition and as to the adequacy of the table of the categories insofar as they are determinations of our consciousness borrowed from the logical functions of judgments in general (as the reviewer does), the system of
the *Critique* must carry with it apodeictic certainty, because it is built on the
proposition that the whole speculative use of our reason never reaches beyond
objects of possible experience. For if it can be proved *that* the categories,
which reason must make use of in all its cognition, can have no other employment whatever than that merely with reference to objects of experience
(in such a way that in this experience the categories make possible merely the
form of thought), then the answer to the question *how* they make such form
of thought possible is indeed important enough for completing this deduction, where possible; but with reference to the main purpose of the system,
namely, the determination of the boundary of pure reason, the answer to *how*
is in no way necessary but is merely meritorious. For this purpose the deduction is already carried far enough when it shows that categories, which are
thought, are nothing but mere forms of judgments insofar as these forms are
applied to intuitions (which with us are always sensible only), and that by
such application our intuitions first of all obtain objects and become cognitions; showing these things already suffices to establish with complete certainty the whole system of the *Critique* proper. Thus Newton's system of
universal gravitation is well established, even though it carries with it the
difficulty that one cannot explain how attraction at a distance is possible.
But difficulties are not doubts. Now, that the foundation remains even without the complete deduction of the categories can be shown from what is
conceded, thus.
475   1. Conceded: The table of the categories completely contains all the pure
concepts of the understanding as well as all the formal operations of the

in the way of discovery or addition; but improvement can be made where anything might be lacking in clearness or thoroughness.

Therefore, the concept of matter had to be carried out through all the four functions of the concepts of the understanding (in four chapters), in each of which a new determination of matter was added. The fundamental determination of a something that is to be an object of the external senses

---

understanding in judgments, from which such pure concepts are derived and from which they also differ in nothing except that in the concept of the understanding, an object is thought as determined in regard to one or the other function of judgments. (E.g., in the categorical judgment "the stone is hard", the "stone" is employed as subject and "hard" as predicate, so that it remains permissible for the understanding to interchange the logical function of these concepts and say "something hard is a stone". On the other hand, when I represent to myself in the object as determined that the stone in every possible determination of an object, and not of the mere concept, must be thought only as subject and the hardness only as predicate, the same logical functions now become pure concepts of the understanding for cognizing objects, namely, substance and accident).

2. Conceded: The understanding by its nature carries with it a priori synthetic principles, by which it subordinates to the categories all objects that might be given to it. Consequently, there must also be a priori intuitions, which contain the requisite conditions for the application of the pure concepts of the understanding, inasmuch as without intuition there is no object with regard to which the logical function can be determined as category, and consequently there is no cognition of any object. Therefore, without pure intuition there is no principle which a priori determines the logical function for such cognition.

3. Conceded: These pure intuitions can never be anything but mere forms of the appearances of the external senses or of the internal sense (space and time), and consequently can be forms only of objects of possible experiences.

It follows that no employment of pure reason can ever concern anything but objects of experience; and inasmuch as nothing empirical can be the condition in a priori principles, these cannot be anything more than principles of the possibility of experience generally. This alone is the true and adequate foundation of the determination of the boundary of pure reason, but is not the solution of the problem as to *how* experience is possible by means of these categories, and only by means of them. Although even without this problem the structure stands firm, this problem nevertheless has great importance, and, as I now see, equally great facility, inasmuch as it can be solved almost by a single conclusion from the precisely determined definition of a judgment in general (an act by which given representations first become cognitions of an object). The obscurity which in this part of the *476*

477

must be motion, for thereby only can these senses be affected. The understanding leads all other predicates which pertain to the nature of matter back to motion; thus natural science is throughout either a pure or an applied doctrine of motion. *The Metaphysical Foundations of Natural Science* may be brought, then, under four main chapters. The first may be called *Phoronomy;* and in it motion is considered as pure quantum, according to its composition, without any quality of the matter. The second may be termed *Dynamics,* and in it motion is regarded as belonging to the quality of the matter under the name of an original moving force. The third emerges under the name of *Mechanics,* and in it matter with this dynamical quality is considered as by its own

---

deduction attaches to my previous treatment, and which I do not disclaim, is attributable to the usual fortune of the understanding in inquiry, the shortest way being commonly not the first which it becomes aware of. Therefore I shall take the earliest opportunity* to make up this defect (which concerns only the manner of the presentation and not the ground of explanation, which is already given correctly there) without my acute reviewer's being placed in the—doubtless to himself—disagreeable necessity of taking refuge in a pre-established harmony because of the surprising agreement of appearances with the laws of the understanding, even though the latter have sources quite different from the former—a remedy far worse than the evil which it is intended to cure and against which it really can avail nothing at all. For from such a preestablished harmony there cannot come the objective necessity that characterizes the pure concepts of the understanding (and the principles of their application to appearances). For example, in the concept of cause as connected with effect, everything remains merely subjectively necessary but is objectively merely chance connection, just as Hume has it when he calls such connection mere illusion through custom. No system in the world can derive this objective necessity ötherwise than from the a priori principles lying at the foundation of the possibility of thought itself, by which alone the cognition of objects whose appearance is given us, i.e., experience, is possible. And supposing that the manner as to *how* experience is thereby possible in the first place could never be adequately explained; it would nevertheless remain indisputably certain *that* experience is possible only through those concepts and, conversely, that those concepts likewise are capable of no meaning or employment in any other reference than to objects of experience.

---

* [In the second edition (1787) of the *Critique,* B 129–169.]

motion to be in relation.[9] The fourth is called *Phenomenology;* and in it matter's motion or rest is determined merely with reference to the mode of representation, or modality, i.e., as an appearance of the external senses.

But beside the internal necessity of distinguishing the metaphysical foundations of the doctrine of body not only from physics, which employs empirical principles, but even from physics' rational premises, which concern the employment of mathematics in physics, there is furthermore an external and, though only accidental, yet important reason for separating its thorough working-out from the general system of metaphysics,[10] and for presenting it systematically as a special whole. For it is permissible to delineate the boundaries of a science not merely according to the constitution of its object and the specific mode of cognition of its object, but also according to the aim that is kept in view as to the further use of the science itself; and one finds that metaphysics has engaged so many heads up till now and will continue to engage them not in order to extend natural knowledge (which comes about much more easily and certainly by observation, experiment, and the application of mathematics to external phenomena), but in order to attain to a knowledge of what lies entirely beyond all the boundaries of experience, namely, God, freedom, and immortality. If these things are so, then one gains when he frees general metaphysics from a shoot springing indeed from its own root but only hindering its regular growth, and plants this shoot apart, without mistaking its origination from metaphysics or ignoring its entire outgrowth from the system of general metaphysics. Doing this does not affect the completeness of the system of general metaphysics but facilitates the uniform progress

[9] [That is, various material objects through their proper motions stand in relation with one another.]

[10] [Contained in the *Critique of Pure Reason.*]

478   of this science toward its goal, if, in all cases where the general doctrine of body is needed, one can call upon the separate system of such a doctrine without encumbering the larger system of metaphysics in general with this general doctrine of body. Furthermore, it is indeed very remarkable (but cannot here be thoroughly entered into) that general metaphysics in all cases where it requires instances (intuitions) in order to provide meaning for its pure concepts of the understanding must always take such instances from the general doctrine of body, i.e., from the form and principles of external intuition;[11] and if these instances are not at hand in their entirety, it gropes, uncertain and trembling, among mere meaningless concepts. Hence there are the well-known disputes, or at least the obscurity in questions, concerning the possibility of an opposition of realities, the possibility of intensive magnitude, etc., with regard to which the understanding is taught only through instances from corporeal nature what the conditions are under which the concepts of the understanding can alone have objective reality, i.e., meaning and truth. And so a separate metaphysics of corporeal nature does excellent and indispensable service to general metaphysics, inasmuch as the former provides instances (cases *in concreto*) in which to realize the concepts and propositions of the latter (properly, transcendental philosophy), i.e., to give to a mere form of thought sense and meaning.

I have in this treatise followed the mathematical method, if not with all strictness (for which more time would have been required than I had to devote to it), at least imitatively. I have done this not in order to obtain a better reception for it through a display of profundity, but because I believe that such a system is quite capable of a mathematical treatment, and that perfection may in time be attained by a cleverer hand when, stimulated by this sketch, mathematical investi-

[11] [Cf. *ibid.*, B 288–294.]

gators of nature may find it not unimportant to treat the metaphysical portion—which cannot be got rid of anyway—as a special fundamental part of general physics, and to bring it into unison with the mathematical doctrine of motion.

Newton, in the preface to his *Mathematical Principles of Natural Philosophy* (after having remarked that geometry requires only two mechanical actions, which it postulates, namely, to describe a straight line and a circle), says: Geometry is proud of being able to produce so much with so little taken from elsewhere.[12] On the other hand, one might say *479* of metaphysics: It stands astonished that with so much offered it by pure mathematics, it can effect so little. Nevertheless, this little is something which even mathematics indispensably requires in its application to natural science; and since mathematics must here necessarily borrow from metaphysics,[13] it need not be ashamed to let itself be seen in the company of the latter.

[12] *Gloriatur geometria, quod tam paucis principiis aliunde petitis tam multa praestet.* Newton, *Prin. Phil. Nat. Math. Praefat.*

[13] [See below, Akademie edition numbers 485–486 (pp. 25–27), Ak. 493–495, 503–508, 518–523. Subsequent cross references to this translation will be made to the marginal Akademie numbers.]

FIRST
CHAPTER

Metaphysical Foundations of Phoronomy

EXPLICATION[14] 1

Matter is the movable in space. That space which is itself movable is called material, or also relative, space; that in which all motion must ultimately be thought (which is itself therefore absolutely immovable) is called pure, or also absolute, space.

Observation 1

Nothing but motion is to be discussed in phoronomy; therefore, no other property than movability is here attributed to the subject of motion, namely, matter. Matter thus endowed can itself be taken, then, as a point. In phoronomy one abstracts from every internal characteristic, hence also from the quantity, of the movable and concerns himself only with motion and what can be regarded as quantity therein (velocity and direction). If the expression "body" is nevertheless sometimes used here, it occurs only to anticipate to some

---

[14] [*Erklärung*. In view of the mathematical format of the book, it might seem that "definition" would be a better translation. However, compare *Critique of Pure Reason*, B 755–760.]

extent the application of the principles of phoronomy to the subsequent more determinate concepts of matter, so that the discourse may be less abstract and more comprehensible.

Observation 2   *481*

If I am to explicate the concept of matter not by a predicate that applies to it as object but only by its relation to the faculty of cognition in which the representation can first of all be given to me, then matter is every object of the external senses; and this would be its mere metaphysical explication. But space would be simply the form of all external sensible intuition (whether such intuition in itself accrues also to the external object that we call matter or remains only in the nature of our sense does not at all here enter into question). In contrast to form, matter would be what in external intuition is an object of sensation and consequently would be the properly empirical part of sensible and external intuition, because matter cannot be given at all a priori. In all experience something must be sensed, and this is the real of sensible intuition. Consequently, the space in which we are to set up experience regarding motions must also be capable of being sensed, i.e., must be indicated by what can be sensed; and this space as the sum total of all objects of experience and itself an object of experience is called empirical space. Now, such space insofar as it is material is itself movable. But a movable space, if its motion is to be capable of being perceived, presupposes again another enlarged material space in which it is movable, and this enlarged space presupposes just as well another, and so on to infinity.

Hence all motion that is an object of experience is merely relative. The space in which motion is perceived is a relative space, which itself moves again, perhaps in an opposite direction, in an enlarged space; therefore, matter moved in reference to the first space may be termed at rest in relation to the second. These variations of the concept of motions continue infinitely with the change of the relative space. To assume an absolute space—i.e., such a space as can be no object of experience because it is not material—as itself given means to assume something that cannot be perceived either in itself or in its consequences (motion in absolute space) for the sake of the possibility of experience, which must [in actuality] always be constituted without such a space. There-fore, absolute space is in itself nothing and is no object at all, but signifies merely every other relative space that I can at any time think of outside a given space, and that I merely can extend beyond each given space to infinity as being such a space as includes this given one, and in which I can assume this given one to be moved. Because I have the enlarged, though still material space only in thought, and because nothing is known to me regarding the matter which indicates this space, so I abstract from the matter and therefore repre-

482 sent the space as a pure, nonempirical, and absolute one. I can compare every empirical space with this absolute one and can represent the former as movable in the latter, which is hence always taken as immovable. To make this absolute space an actual thing means to mistake the logical univer-sality of any space, with which I can compare each empir-ical space as being included in it, for a physical universal-ity of actual compass, and to misunderstand reason in its idea.

In conclusion I observe further that inasmuch as the mov-ability of an object in space cannot be cognized a priori and without instruction from experience, such movability just for that reason could not be counted by me in the *Critique of Pure Reason* among the pure concepts of the understanding; and observe that this concept as empirical can find a place only in a natural science insofar as it is applied metaphysics, which occupies itself with a concept given through experi-ence, though according to a priori principles.

EXPLICATION 2

The motion of a thing is the change of its external relations to a given space.

Observation 1

I have already laid the concept of motion at the basis of the concept of matter. For since I wanted to determine the very concept of matter independently of the concept of extension and thus could consider matter as a point, so I was permitted to allow the use of the common explication of motion as change of place. Now, inasmuch as the concept of matter is to be explicated universally, and hence is to be explicated in a way suitable also for moved bodies, that definition is inadequate. The place of every body is a point. If one wants to determine the distance of the moon from the earth, then he wants to know the distance between their places. And to this end one does not measure from any arbitrary point of the surface or interior of the earth to any arbitrary point of the moon, but takes the shortest line from the center of the one to the center of the other; hence in each of these bodies there is only one point that constitutes its place. Now, a body can move without changing its place, as does the earth in turning on its axis. But its relation to external space hereby changes nonetheless; for it turns, e.g., in twenty-four hours, its various sides toward the moon, and from this turning all kinds of variable effects result on the earth. Only of a movable, i.e., physical, point can one say: motion is always a change of place. Contrary to this explication, one might remember that internal motion, e.g., fermentation, is not in-   *483* cluded in it; but the thing that one says is moved must according to this explication be regarded as a unit. The fact that matter, e.g., a cask of beer, is moved therefore means something other than the fact that the beer in the cask is in motion. The motion of a thing is not identical with the motion in this thing, but the case under consideration here is only the former. However, the application of the former concept of motion to the latter case is subsequently easy.

Observation 2

Motions may be progressive or rotatory (without change of place). They may either enlarge their space or be limited to a given space. Those that enlarge their space are rectilinear motions or even curvilinear ones that do not return in upon themselves. Those limited to a given space are such as return in upon themselves, and these are again either circular or oscillatory, i.e., round or swaying motions. The first cover the very same space always in the same direction, the second the same space always alternately in an opposite direction, like a swaying pendulum. To both belong, in addition, trembling (*motus tremulus*), which is not a progressive motion of a body but a reciprocating motion of a matter that does not thereby change its position as a whole, such as the vibrations of a struck bell or the tremblings of the air set in motion by the peal. I merely make mention of these different kinds of motion in phoronomy because in the case of all that are not progressive the word "velocity" is generally used in another sense than in the case of those that are, as the following observation shows.

Observation 3

In every motion, velocity and direction are the two moments for consideration, when one abstracts from all other properties of the movable. I presuppose here the usual definition of both, but that of direction requires in addition various limitations. A body moved in a circle changes its direction continuously, so that until its return to the point from which it started, all direction is comprised in a plane of merely possible directions; and yet one says that it moves always in the same direction, e.g., a planet from evening till morning.

But what is here the side toward which the motion is directed?[15] This question is related to the following one: upon what rests the internal difference of spirals which are otherwise similar and even equal, except that one species winds to the right and the other to the left? Or upon what rests the internal difference of the winding of pole beans and of hops, the *484* former running around its pole like a corkscrew, or, as sailors would express it, against the sun, the latter running around its pole with the sun? The concept of this internal difference is one that indeed admits of being constructed, but as concept does not at all admit of being clarified by universal marks in the discursive mode of cognition. In things themselves (e.g., in the case of those rare human beings in whom, upon dissection, all their parts agree according to the physiological rule with those of other human beings, but all the viscera are found displaced to the right or to the left, contrary to the usual order) there can be no conceivable difference in the internal consequences. And yet there is a real mathematical and indeed internal difference, whereby two circular motions differing in direction but in all other respects alike nevertheless do correspond, although they are not completely identical. I have elsewhere[16] pointed out that since this difference admits indeed of being given in intuition, but does not at all admit of being brought to clear concepts and therefore of being intelligibly explicated (*dari, non intelligi*[17]), it affords a good confirmative ground of proof for the proposition that space in general does not belong to the properties or relations of things in themselves, which would

[15] [Today in this case one would say, what is here the sense of the motion.]

[16] [See *Prolegomena,* §13, Akademie edition 285–286.]

[17] ["Given, but not understood."]

necessarily have to admit of reduction to objective concepts, but belongs merely to the subjective form of our sensible intuition of things or relations, which must remain wholly unknown to us as regards what they may be in themselves. But this is a digression from our present business, in which we must quite necessarily treat space as a property of the things we are considering, namely, corporeal entities, because these themselves are only phenomena of the external senses and need to be explicated here only as such. As far as the concept of velocity is concerned, this expression also sometimes acquires in usage a variable meaning. We say that the earth rotates on its axis more rapidly than the sun, because it does so in a shorter time, although the motion of the sun is much more rapid. The circulation of the blood of a small bird is much more rapid than that of a man, although the flowing motion in the bird doubtless has less velocity; and so it is also in the case of the vibrations of elastic matters. The brevity of the time of return, whether of a circular or of an oscillating motion, constitutes the ground of this usage, in which no wrong is done if only misinterpretation is otherwise avoided. For this mere increase in the speed of return without increase of spatial velocity has special and very important effects in nature; perhaps there has not yet been enough notice taken of this fact in regard to the circulation of the fluids of animals. In phoronomy we use the word "velocity" merely in a spatial signification, $C = \frac{S^{18}}{T}$.

485   EXPLICATION 3

Rest is permanent presence (*praesentia perdurabilis*) in the same place; permanent is what exists throughout a time, i.e., endures.

[18] [*Celeritas* $= \frac{Spatium}{Tempus}$, Velocity $= \frac{Space}{Time}$.]

Observation

A body that is in motion is for a moment in every point of the line that it traverses. The question is, now, whether it rests at the point or moves. Doubtless one will say the latter, for it is present at this point only insofar as it moves. But let us suppose the motion in this way: O—————O · · O, the body

                  A   B   a

describes the line AB forwards [from A to B] and backwards from B to A with uniform velocity in such a way that, since the moment it is at B is common to both motions, the motion from A to B is described in half a second and that from B to A also in half a second but both together in a whole second, so that not the smallest portion of time has been expended on the presence of the body at B. And so without the least increase in these motions, the latter, which occurred in the direction BA, will be able to be changed into a motion in the direction Ba, which lies in a straight line with AB; accordingly, the body while it is at B must be regarded not as at rest but as moved. Therefore in the former oscillatory motion it would also have to be regarded as moved at the point B. But this is impossible because, in accordance with what has been assumed, only one moment belongs both to the motion AB and to the equal motion BA, which is opposed to the former and is conjoined with it in one and the same moment. Consequently, if complete lack of motion constitutes the concept of rest, then in the uniform motion Aa the fact that the body is at rest must hold at every point, e.g., at B; but this contradicts the above assertion [that the body is in motion at the point B]. On the other hand, let the line AB be represented as erected over the point A, so that a body rising from A to B, after having lost its motion by means of gravity at the point B, would fall back again from B to A. Now, I ask whether the body at B can be regarded as moved or as at rest? Doubtless one will say at rest, because all previous motion has been taken from it after it has reached this point, and then a uniform motion back is next to follow, but is not yet present; this lack of motion, one will add, is rest. However, in the first case of an assumed uniform motion, the motion BA could not begin otherwise than by the

486   previous cessation of the motion AB and by the nonexistence of the motion from B to A, with the result that at B there was a lack of all motion; and according to the usual explication, rest would have to be assumed. But it must, nevertheless, not be assumed, because at a given velocity no body may be thought of as at rest in any point of its uniform motion. Upon what, then, is the claim of rest based in the second case, since this rising and falling are likewise separated from one another only by a moment? The ground for this claim lies in the fact that the latter motion is not thought of as uniform with the given velocity but as being at first uniformly retarded and afterwards uniformly accelerated, in such a way that the velocity at the point B is not wholly retarded, but only up to a degree that is smaller than any assignable velocity. If the body with such velocity were not to fall back but, rather, its line of fall BA were to be placed in the direction Ba, and hence if it were to be considered as still rising, then it would, as with a mere moment of velocity (the resistance of gravity being disregarded), traverse uniformly in any assignable time, however great, a space smaller than any assignable space. Hence it would not at all change its place (for any possible experience) in all eternity. Consequently, it is put into a state of enduring presence in the same place, i.e., of rest, although owing to the continuous influence of gravity, i.e., the change of this state, the rest is immediately abolished. To be in a permanent state and to persist therein (if nothing else disturbs this state) are two distinct concepts, and one does not impede the other. Therefore, rest cannot be explicated by lack of motion, which, as $= 0$, does not at all admit of being constructed but must be explicated by permanent presence in the same place. Since this concept can be con-

structed by the representation of a motion with infinitely small velocity throughout a finite time, it can therefore be used for the subsequent application of mathematics to nat-ural science.

EXPLICATION 4

To construct the concept of a composite motion means to present a priori in intuition a motion insofar as it arises from two or more given motions united in one movable thing.

Observation

The construction of concepts requires that the condition of their presentation not be borrowed from experience, and hence that there not be presupposed certain forces whose *487* existence is deducible only from experience, or, in general, that the condition of the construction must not itself be a concept which cannot at all be given a priori in intuition, as, for instance, the concept of cause and effect, or action and resistance, etc. Now, it is here especially noteworthy that phoronomy throughout has as its object primarily the construction of motions in general as quantities. Since phoronomy takes matter merely as something movable and hence does not at all consider any quantity of this movable thing, it must a priori determine these motions solely as quantities according to their velocity, as well as their direction, and indeed their composition. For this much must be determined entirely a priori and indeed through intuition on behalf of applied mathematics. For the rules of the connection of motions through physical causes, i.e., forces, never admit of being fundamentally expounded before the principles of their composition in general are previously mathematically laid down as a foundation.

PRINCIPLE

Every motion as object of a possible experience can be viewed at will either as motion of a body in a space that is at rest, or as rest of the body and motion of the space in the opposite direction with equal velocity.

Observation

To experience the motion of a body requires that not only the body but also the space in which it moves be objects of external experience—hence, that they be material. Therefore, an absolute motion, i.e., a motion referred to an immaterial space, is utterly incapable of being experienced and is hence nothing at all for us (even if one might want to grant that absolute space is something in itself). But in all relative motion the space itself, because it is assumed to be material, may be represented as at rest or as moved. The first[19] occurs when, beyond the space with reference to which I regard a body as moved, there is no more extended space that includes this space (as when in the cabin of a ship I see a ball moved on a table). The second occurs when outside this space there is another space that includes this one (as, in the case mentioned, the bank of the river), since with regard to the riverbank I can view the nearest space (the cabin) as moved and the body itself [the ball] as at rest. Now, respecting an empirically given space, however extended it may be, it is utterly impossible to determine whether or not this space is itself moved with reference to a still greater space enclosing it. Hence for all experience and for every inference from experience, it must be all the same whether I want to consider a body as moved, or else consider the body as at rest and the space as moved in the opposite direc-

488

---

[19] [The space represented as at rest.]

tion with an equal velocity. Furthermore, since absolute space is nothing for any possible experience, these concepts are equivalent: whether I say that a body moves with reference to this given [empirical] space in this direction with this velocity, or whether I think of the body as at rest and want to ascribe all the motion to this space, but in an opposite direction. For the one concept[20] is quite the same as the other, and there is no possible instance of the latter being different from the former; only with regard to the connection we want to give the latter in the understanding is it different [from the former].

Moreover, we cannot in any experience whatever specify a fixed point by reference to which there would be determined what absolute motion and absolute rest should mean. For everything given us in this way[21] is material, and is hence movable, and (since in space we know of no extreme limit of possible experience) is perhaps also actually moved without our being able to perceive this motion. Regarding the motion of a body in empirical space, I can assign one part of the given velocity to the body and the other part to the space, but in the opposite direction. The whole possible experience concerning the results of these two combined motions is equivalent to thinking of the body alone as moved with the entire velocity, or thinking of the body as at rest and the space as moved with the entire velocity in the opposite direction. I here assume all motions to be rectilinear. For as concerns nonrectilinear ones, whether I am warranted in regarding the body as moved (e.g., the earth in its daily rotation) and the surrounding space (the starry heavens) as at rest, or the latter as moved and the former as at rest, is not in all respects equivalent; this will be treated in particular in the sequel.[22] In phoronomy, then, where I consider the motion

[20] [Namely, the body moved and the space at rest.]

[21] [That is, in experience.]

[22] ["Phenomenology," Ak. 556–558, 560–562.]

of a body only in relation to space (upon whose motion or rest the body has no influence at all), it is quite undetermined and arbitrary whether I attribute to the body or to the space any or all or how much of the velocity of the given motion. Later in mechanics, where a moved body is to be considered in active relation to other bodies in the space of its motion, this[23] will be no longer so completely equivalent, as will be shown in the proper place.[24]

489   EXPLICATION 5

The composition of motion is the representation of the motion of a point as identical with two or more motions of the point combined.

Observation

Since in phoronomy I cognize matter by no other property than its movability and hence may consider matter itself only as a point, the motion can be considered only as the description of a space. But it is considered in such a way that I pay attention not merely to the space described, as in geometry, but also to the time involved therein and hence to the velocity with which a point describes the space. Phoronomy is, then, the pure doctrine (*mathesis*) of the quantity of motions. The determinate concept of a quantity is the concept of the production of the representation of an object through the composition of the homogeneous. Now, since nothing is homogeneous with motion except motion, so phoronomy is a doctrine of the composition of the motions of the same point according to their direction and velocity, i.e., the representation of a single motion as one that comprises within itself simultaneously two or even several motions, or else

[23] [That is, whether the motion is attributed to the body or to the space.]
[24] ["Mechanics," Ak. 544–550.]

the representation of two motions of the same point simultaneously insofar as they together constitute one motion (that
is, they are identical with this motion), and not insofar as
they produce the latter in the way that causes produce their
effect. In order to find the motion arising from the composition of several motions—or of as many as one wants—one
has only, as with the production of all quantities, first to
seek out that motion which is under given conditions compounded from two motions; thereupon this is compounded
with a third; and so on. Consequently, the doctrine of the
composition of all motions is reducible to the composition
of two. But two motions of one and the same point which
are found simultaneously at this same point can be distinguished in a twofold manner, and as such can be combined in three ways at the point. First, they occur at the same
time either in one and the same line or in different lines;
the latter are motions comprising an angle. Those occurring
in one and the same line are either contrary to one another
in direction or keep the same direction. Since all these motions are considered as occurring simultaneously, there results immediately from the relation of the lines, i.e., of the
spaces described by the motions in equal time, the relation
of the velocities also. Hence there are three cases. (1) Two
motions (they may be of equal or unequal velocities) combined in one body in the same direction are to constitute
a resultant composite motion. (2) Two motions of the same   *490*
point (of equal or unequal velocity) combined in opposite
directions are to constitute through their composition a third
motion in the same line. (3) Two motions of a point, with
equal or unequal velocities, but in different lines that comprise an angle, are considered to be compounded.

PROPOSITION

The composition of two motions of one and the same
point can only be thought of by one of them being repre-

sented in absolute space, but instead of the second motion being so represented, a motion of the relative space in the opposite direction and with the same velocity is represented as being identical with the first motion.

Proof

First case: Two motions in the same line and direction belong simultaneously to one and the same point.

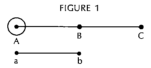

FIGURE 1

Let two velocities AB and ab be represented as contained in one velocity of the motion. Let these velocities be assumed for the time being to be equal, AB = ab; in this case I assert that they cannot be represented simultaneously at the same point in one and the same space (whether absolute or relative). For inasmuch as the lines AB and ab, which denote the velocities, are, strictly speaking, the spaces which are traversed in equal times; so the composition of these spaces AB and ab = BC, and hence the line AC (as the sum of the spaces), must express the sum of both velocities. But the parts AB and BC do not, individually, represent the velocity = ab; for they are not traversed in the same time as ab. Hence the double line AC, which is traversed in the same time as the line ab, does not represent the double velocity of the latter, as was nevertheless required. Hence the composition of two velocities in one direction in the same space cannot be presented intuitively.

491   On the other hand, if I represent the body A as moved in absolute space with the velocity AB and in addition I give to the relative space a velocity ab = AB in the opposite direction ba = CB, then this is the same as my having given the latter velocity to the body in the direction AB (Principle). But the body in this case moves in the same time through the sum of the lines AB and BC, their sum being equal to 2ab, and in this time it would have traversed the line ab = AB only; and yet its velocity is represented as the sum of the two equal velocities AB and ab, which is what was required.

Second case: Two motions in exactly opposite directions are to be combined at one and the same point.

FIGURE 2

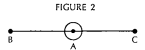

Let AB be one of these motions and AC the other in the opposite direction; we here assume the velocity of the latter motion to be equal to that of the first. In this case the very thought of representing two such motions in one and the same space at the very same point as simultaneous would be impossible, and hence the case of such a composition of motions would itself be impossible too, which is contrary to the assumption.

On the other hand, let the motion AB be thought of as in absolute space; and instead of the motion AC in this absolute space, let the opposite motion CA of the relative space be thought of with the very same velocity, which (according to our Principle) is fully equal to the motion AC and can hence be entirely substituted for it. In this case two exactly opposite and equal motions of the same point at the same time may very well be presented. Now, inasmuch as the relative space is moved with the same velocity CA = AB in the same direction with the point A; so this point, or the body present therein, does not change its place with regard to the relative space, i.e., a body moved in two exactly opposite directions with equal velocity rests, or, generally expressed, its motion is equal to the difference of the velocities in the direction of the greater one (and this fact easily follows from what has already been proved).

Third case: Two motions of the same point are repre-   *492* sented as combined according to directions that enclose an angle.

FIGURE 3

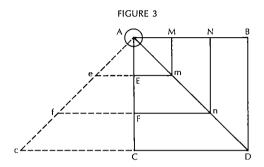

The two given motions are AB and AC, whose velocity and directions are expressed by these lines, but the angle enclosed by the latter is expressed by BAC (it may, as here, be a right angle, but it may also be any arbitrary oblique angle). Now, if these two motions are to occur simultaneously in the directions AB and AC and indeed in one and the same space, then they would not be able to occur simultaneously in both these lines AB and AC, but only in lines running parallel to these. It would therefore have to be assumed that one of these motions produced a change in the other (namely, the deviation from the given course), although the directions remained mutually the same. But this is contrary to the proposition's assumption, which indicates by the word "composition" that both the given motions are contained in a third and hence are identical with this third, and not that a third is produced by one of them changing the other.

On the other hand, let the motion AC be assumed as taking place in absolute space; but instead of the motion AB, let the motion of the relative space in the opposite direction be assumed. Let the line AC be divided into three equal parts, AE, EF, FC. Now, while the body A in absolute space traverses the line AE; the relative space, and with it

the point E, traverses the space Ee = MA. While the body
traverses the two parts together = AF; the relative space,   *493*
and with it the point F, describes the line Ff = NA. While,
finally, the body traverses the whole line AC; the relative
space, and with it the point C, describes the line Cc = BA.
All this is the same as though the body A had traversed in
these three divisions of time the lines Em, Fn, and CD = AM,
AN, AB, and in the whole time in which it traverses AC had
traversed the line CD = AB. Therefore, it is at the last moment at the point D and in this whole time is gradually at all
points of the diagonal line AD, which, accordingly, expresses
the direction as well as the velocity of the composite
motion.

Observation 1

Geometrical construction requires that one quantity be identical with the other, or that two quantities in composition
be identical with a third and not that they produce the third
as causes, which would be mechanical construction. Complete similarity and equality insofar as they can be cognized
only in intuition is congruity. All geometrical construction of
complete identity rests on congruity. This congruity of two
combined motions with a third (as the *motu compositio*[25] itself) can never take place when the two former are represented in one and the same space, e.g., relative space. Hence
all attempts to prove the foregoing proposition in its three
cases have always been mechanical solutions only, inasmuch, namely, as one let moving causes, by which a given
motion was combined with another, produce a third motion.
Such attempts, however, were not proofs that the former motions were identical with the latter motion and that because
of this identity they admitted of being presented in pure
intuition a priori.

[25] ["Composition of motion."]

Observation 2

When, for instance, a velocity AC is termed double, nothing else can be understood thereby but that it consists of two simple and equal velocities AB and BC (see Fig. 1). But if a double velocity be explicated by saying that it is a motion whereby a doubly great space is traversed in the same time, then something is here assumed which is not a matter of course, namely, that two equal velocities admit of being combined in the same way as two equal spaces. But it is not of itself obvious that a given velocity consists of smaller velocities and a speed of slownesses in the same way that a space consists of smaller spaces. For the parts of the velocity are not external to one another as the parts of the space are; and if the former are to be considered as quantity, then the concept of their quantity, since it is intensive, must be constructed in a way different from that of the extensive
494   quantity of space. But this construction is possible in no other way than by the mediate composition of two equal motions, one of which is that of the body; the other, that of the relative space in the opposite direction, and just for this reason, completely identical with an equal motion of the body in the previous direction. For in the same direction two equal velocities do not admit of being combined in one body except through external moving causes, e.g., a ship carries the body with one of these velocities, while another moving force immovably combined with the ship impresses upon the body the second velocity, which is equal to the previous one. In all this it must always be assumed that the body maintains itself in free motion with the first velocity when the second velocity is added; this is a natural law of moving forces, and this law cannot at all come into consideration when the question is merely how the concept of velocity is constructed as a quantity. So much for the addition of velocities to one another. But when the question concerns the sub-

traction of one velocity from another, such substraction can indeed easily be thought of if the possibility of a velocity as quantity by addition has once been granted. But the concept of this subtraction cannot so easily be constructed. For to this end two opposite motions must be combined in one body; but how is this to happen? Immediately, i.e., with regard to the same resting space, there is no possibility of thinking of two equal motions in opposite directions in the same body. But the representation of the impossibility of these two motions in one body is not the concept of its rest but is the concept of the impossibility of the construction of this composition of opposite motions; nevertheless, this composition is assumed in the proposition to be possible. But this construction is not otherwise possible than by the combination of the motion of the body with the motion of the space, as has been proved. Finally, as concerns the composition of two motions whose direction encloses an angle, they likewise cannot be thought of in the body by reference to one and the same space unless one of the motions is assumed to be produced by an external, continuously inflowing force (e.g., a vessel bearing the body onward) and the other motion is assumed to maintain itself unaltered. Or to express it generally, one must have as a basis moving forces and the production of a third motion from two combined forces. This is indeed the mechanical execution of what a concept contains, but is not the mathematical construction of the composition. Such a construction should only make intuitive what the object (as quantum) is and not how the object may be produced by nature or art through certain tools and forces. In order to determine the relation of motions to other ones as quantity, their composition must take place according to the rules of congruity. This is possible *495* in all three cases only by means of the space's motion which is congruent with one of the two given motions, whereby both are congruent with the composite motion.

Observation 3

Thus phoronomy, not as pure doctrine of motion, but merely as pure doctrine of the quantity of motion, in which matter is thought of according to no other property than that of mere movability, contains nothing but this single proposition, carried out in the three cases cited, concerning the composition of motion, and indeed concerning the possibility of rectilinear motion alone, not of curvilinear. For since in this latter the motion is continuously changed (in direction), a cause of this change, which cannot be merely space, must be introduced. But the fact that one usually understands by the designation "composite motion" only the single case where the directions of such a motion enclose an angle does some detriment to the principle of the division of a pure philosophical science in general, although not to physics. For as far as physics is concerned, all three cases treated in the above proposition can be presented adequately in the third case alone. For if the angle enclosing the two given motions is thought of as infinitely small, it contains the first case. But if the angle is represented as only infinitely little different from a single straight line, it contains the second case. Consequently, all three cases mentioned by us can indeed be given in the familiar proposition concerning composite motion as in a universal formula. But in this way one could not learn to comprehend a priori the quantitative doctrine of motion according to its parts; such comprehension is useful for many purposes.

If anyone wants to connect the aforementioned three parts of the phoronomic proposition with the schema of the division of all pure concepts of the understanding, namely, with that of the division of the concept of quantity, he will observe the following. Since the concept of quantity always contains the concept of the composition of the homogeneous, the doctrine of the composition of motions is at the same time the pure doctrine of quantity therein. And indeed this doctrine according to all three moments[26] furnished by space, namely, the unity of line and direction, the plurality of directions in one and the same line, and finally the totality of directions as well as of lines, according to which the motion can take place, contains the determination of all possible motion as quantum, although motion's quantity (in a movable point) consists merely in velocity. This observation is useful only in transcendental philosophy.

[26] [Cf. *Critique of Pure Reason,* B 106.]

SECOND CHAPTER

Metaphysical Foundations of Dynamics

EXPLICATION 1

Matter is the movable insofar as it fills a space. To fill a space means to resist everything movable that strives by its motion to press into a certain space. A space that is not filled is an empty space.

Observation

This is, now, the dynamical explication of the concept of matter. This explication presupposes the phoronomic one but adds to it a property that is related as cause to an effect, namely, the capacity of resisting a motion within a certain space. This property could not come into consideration in the foregoing science, even when we dealt with the motions of one and the same point in opposite directions. This filling of space keeps a certain space free from the intrusion of any other movable thing when its motion is directed to any place within this space. Now, we must investigate what matter's resistance directed to all sides is based upon and what this resistance is. But one sees already from the preceding explication that matter is not here considered as resisting when it is driven from its place and is thus itself moved (this case will hereafter come into consideration as mechanical resist-

ance), but it is considered as resisting only when the space   *497*
of its own extension is to be diminished. One uses the words
"to occupy a space", i.e., to be immediately present in all
its points, in order to indicate thereby the extension of a
thing in space. But there is not determined in this concept
what action, or whether any action at all, arises from this
presence as it resists other presences that try to press into it;
or whether this concept signifies merely a space without
matter insofar as such a space is a sum total of several spaces,
just as one can say of every geometrical figure that it occupies a space (it is extended); or even whether there is
something in space necessitating another movable to penetrate deeper into this something (attracting others). Inasmuch, I say, as all of this is undetermined in the concept of
occupying a space, "to fill a space" is therefore a closer determination of the concept "to occupy a space".

PROPOSITION 1

Matter fills a space, not by its mere existence, but by a special
moving force.

Proof

Penetration into a space (in the initial moment this is called
the endeavor to penetrate) is a motion. The resistance to
motion is the reason why motion diminishes or even changes
into rest. Now, nothing can be combined with any motion
as lessening or destroying it but another motion of the same
movable thing in the opposite direction (phoronomic proposition). Consequently, the resistance offered by a matter[27]

[27] [Matter in particular usually means merely body. "A matter" as Kant
ordinarily employs this expression does not mean "a particular kind of matter" but "a piece of matter of any kind whatever". The context should make
clear whether "a matter" means "a piece of matter" or "a particular kind of
matter".]

in the space that it fills to all intrusion by another matter is a cause of the motion of this other matter in the opposite direction. But the cause of a motion is called moving force. Consequently, matter fills its space by moving force and not by its mere existence.

Observation

Lambert[28] and others called the property of matter by which it fills a space its solidity (a rather ambiguous expression) and maintained that such solidity must be assumed in everything which exists (substance), at least in the external sensible world. According to their concepts the presence of some-
498   thing real in space must by its very concept carry with it this resistance and hence does so according to the principle of contradiction, and must exclude the coexistence of anything else in the space in which such a real thing is present. But the principle of contradiction does not repel[29] any matter that advances in order to penetrate into a space in which another matter is to be found. Only when I attribute to that which occupies a space a force to repel every external mov-able thing that approaches it, do I understand how a con-tradiction is involved when the space which a thing occupies is penetrated by another thing of the same kind. Here the mathematician has assumed something as an initial datum of the construction of the concept of matter, but this some-thing does not admit of being further constructed. Now, he can indeed begin his construction from any datum he pleases, without involving himself also in explicating this datum in turn; but he is nevertheless not thereby authorized to explicate this datum as something wholly incapable of any

[28] [Johann Heinrich Lambert (1728–1777) was a German mathematician, physicist, astronomer, and philosopher. He wrote *Photometry, Cosmological Letters, New Organon,* and other works.]

[29] [An example of Kantian wit.]

mathematical construction in order thereby to prevent a return to the first principles of natural science.

EXPLICATION 2

Attractive force is that moving force whereby a matter can be the cause of the approach of other matter to itself (or, equivalently, whereby it resists the withdrawal of other matter from itself).

Repulsive force is that whereby a matter can be the cause of making other matter withdraw from itself (or, equivalently, whereby it resists the approach of other matter to itself). The latter we shall also sometimes call driving force, and the former, drawing.

Note

These are the only two moving forces that can be thought of. For all motion which one matter can impress on another must always be regarded as imparted in the straight line between two points, since with respect to such motion each of these matters is considered merely as a point. But in this straight line only two kinds of motion are possible: one by which the above points recede from one another and a second by which they approach one another. But the force which is the cause of the first motion is called repulsive and that *499* of the second attractive. Consequently, there can be thought only these two kinds of forces, to which as such all the forces of motion in material nature must be reduced.

PROPOSITION 2

Matter fills its space by the repulsive forces of all its parts, i.e., by its own force of extension, which has a determinate degree, beyond which can be thought smaller or greater degrees to infinity.

Proof

Matter fills a space only by moving force (Proposition 1) and indeed by such a force as resists the penetration, i.e., the approach, of other matter. Now, this is a repulsive force (Explication 2). Therefore, matter fills its space only by repulsive forces, and indeed by the repulsive forces of all its parts, because otherwise a part of its space would not be filled (against the assumption) but would only be enclosed. But the force of something extended by virtue of the repulsion of all its parts is a force of extension (expansive). Therefore, matter fills its space only by its own force of extension; and this was the first point. Beyond every given force a greater must admit of being thought of, for that beyond which there is no greater possible would be one whereby in a finite time an infinite space would be traversed (which is impossible). Further, below every given moving force a smaller must admit of being thought of (for the smallest would be that by whose infinite addition to itself throughout any given time no finite velocity could be generated, but this means the lack of all moving force). Therefore, below every given degree of a moving force a still smaller degree must always be able to be given; and this is the second point. Hence the force of extension, whereby all matter fills its space, has its degree, which is never the greatest or smallest, but beyond which can be found greater as well as smaller to infinity.

500   Note 1

The expansive force of matter is also called elasticity. Now, since this force is the basis upon which rests the filling of space as an essential property of all matter, this elasticity must be termed original, because it cannot be derived from any other property of matter. All matter is, accordingly, originally elastic.

Note 2

There can be found beyond every extensive force a greater moving force which can work against the former and would thus diminish the space that the extensive force is striving to expand; in such a case this greater moving force would be termed a compressive one. Because of this fact, for every matter there must be able to be found a compressive force capable of driving this matter from every space that it fills into a smaller space.

EXPLICATION 3

A matter in its motion penetrates another when the former, by compression, completely abolishes the space of the latter's extension.

Observation

When the piston of an air pump's barrel that is filled with air is driven continually closer to the bottom, the air-matter is compressed. Now, if this compression could be carried so far that the piston completely touched the bottom (without the least bit of air escaping), then the air-matter would be penetrated. For the matters between which it is leave no space for it, and thus it would be found between the bottom and the piston without occupying a space. This penetrability of matter by external compressive forces, if anyone were willing to assume or even to think of such penetrability, would be termed mechanical. I have reasons for distinguishing, by such a limitation, this penetrability of matter from another kind, the concept of which is perhaps just as impossible; I may hereafter have occasion to make some mention of this other kind of penetrability.[30]

501   # PROPOSITION 3

Matter can be compressed to infinity; but it can never be penetrated by other matter, regardless of how great the pressing force of this other may be.

Proof

An original force whereby a matter endeavors to extend itself everywhere in a given space that it occupies must be greater when enclosed in a smaller space, and must be infinite when compressed into an infinitely small space. Now, for any given extensive force of matter there can be found a greater compressive force that drives this matter into a smaller space, and so on to infinity; this was the first point. But in order to penetrate the matter, its compression into an infinitely small space would be required, and hence an infinitely compressive force would be required; but such a force is impossible. Consequently, a matter cannot be penetrated by the compression of any other matter; this is the second point.

Observation

I have assumed at the very beginning of this proof that the more an extensive force is constricted so much the more strongly must it counteract. Now, this would not indeed hold for every kind of elastic forces that are only derivative; but this can be postulated of matter possessing essential

[30] [Cf. below, Ak. 530–532.]

elasticity insofar as it is matter in general filling a space. For expansive force exercised from all points toward all sides constitutes the very concept of elasticity. But the same quantum of expanding forces brought into a narrower space must in every point of the space repel so much the more strongly in inverse proportion to the smallness of the space in which a certain quantum of force diffuses its efficacy.

EXPLICATION 4

The impenetrability of matter resting on resistance, which increases proportionally to the degree of compression, I term relative; but that which rests on the assumption that   *502* matter, as such, is capable of no compression at all is called absolute impenetrability. The filling of space with absolute impenetrability may be called mathematical; that with merely relative impenetrability, dynamical.

Observation 1

According to the mere mathematical concept of impenetrability (which assumes no moving force as originally inherent in matter), no matter is capable of compression except insofar as it contains within itself empty spaces. Hence matter, insofar as it is matter, resists all penetration unconditionally and with absolute necessity. According to our discussion of this property, however, impenetrability rests on a physical basis; for the extensive force makes matter itself, as something extended filling its space, first of all possible. But this force has a degree which can be overcome, and hence matter's space of extension can be diminished, i.e., its space can be penetrated in a certain measure by a given compressive force, but only in such a way that complete penetration is impossible, inasmuch as such penetration would require an infinite compressive force; because of all this, the filling of space must be regarded only as relative impenetrability.

Observation 2

Absolute impenetrability is indeed nothing more or less than a *qualitas occulta*. For one asks, what is the reason why matters cannot penetrate one another in their motion? He receives the answer, because they are impenetrable. The appeal to repulsive force is free of this reproach. For although this force likewise cannot be further explicated according to its possibility and must hence be admitted as a fundamental one, it nevertheless yields the concept of an active cause and of the laws of this cause in accordance with which the effect, namely, the resistance in the filled space, can be estimated according to the degrees of this effect.

EXPLICATION 5

Material substance is that in space which of itself, i.e., separated from all else existing outside it in space, is movable.
503   The motion of a part of matter whereby it ceases to be a part [of that matter] is separation. The separation of the parts of matter is physical division.

Observation

The concept of substance signifies the ultimate subject of existence, i.e., that which does not itself in turn belong merely as predicate to the existence of another. Now, matter is the subject of everything in space that can be counted as belonging to the existence of things; for besides matter no subject would otherwise admit of being thought of except space itself, which is, however, a concept that does not contain anything at all existent but contains merely the necessary conditions of the external relation of possible objects of the external senses. Therefore, matter as the movable in space is substance therein. But just in the same way all parts of matter will likewise be substances insofar as one can say of them that they are themselves subjects and not merely predicates of other matters, and hence these parts themselves will in turn have to be called matter. They are themselves subjects if they are of themselves movable, and hence beside their association with other adjacent parts are also something existing in space. Therefore, the proper movability of matter or of any part thereof is at the same time a proof that this movable thing, and every movable part thereof, is substance.

PROPOSITION 4

Matter is divisible to infinity, and indeed into parts each of which is again matter.[31]

Proof

Matter is impenetrable by its original force of extension (Proposition 3), but this force of extension is only the consequence of the repulsive forces of each point in a space filled with matter. Now, the space that matter fills is mathematically divisible to infinity, i.e., its parts can be differentiated to infinity, although they cannot be moved and, consequently, cannot be separated (according to demonstrations of geometry). But in a space filled with matter every part of the space contains repulsive force to counteract on all sides all remaining parts, and hence to repel them and likewise be

---

[31] [This proposition, its proof, and the following two observations should be compared with the Second Antinomy in the *Critique of Pure Reason,* B 462–471, 518–535, 551–560.]

repelled by them, i.e., to be moved to a distance from them.
504 Hence every part of a space filled by matter is of itself movable and is therefore separable by physical division from the
remaining parts, insofar as they are material substance.
Consequently, as far as the mathematical divisibility of space
filled by a matter reaches, thus far does the possible physical
division of the substance that fills the space likewise reach.
But the mathematical divisibility extends to infinity, and
consequently also the physical, i.e., all matter is divisible
to infinity and indeed is divisible into parts each of which
is itself in turn material substance.

Observation 1

By the proof of the infinite divisibility of space, that of matter
has not by a long way been proved, if one has not previously
shown that in every part of space there is material substance,
i.e., that parts movable of themselves are to be found. For
if a monadist might want to assume that matter consists of
physical points each of which (for this reason) has no movable parts but yet fills a space by mere repulsive force, he
would be able to grant that this space, but not the substance
acting in it, is at the same time divided, and hence that the
sphere of the substance's activity is divided, but not that the
active movable subject itself is at the same time divided by
the division of the space. Accordingly, he would compound
matter from physically indivisible parts and yet allow it to
occupy space in a dynamical way.

By the above proof, however, this subterfuge is completely
taken away from the monadist. For from this proof it is clear
that in a filled space there can be no point that does not
itself on all sides repel in the same way as it is repelled, i.e.,
as a reacting subject, of itself movable, existing outside of
every other repelling point; and it is clear that the hypothesis
of a point filling a space by mere driving force and not by
means of other likewise repulsive forces is completely im-

possible. In order to make this fact and thereby also the proof of the preceding proposition intuitable, let it be assumed that A is the place of a monad in space, that ab is the

FIGURE 4

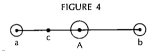

diameter of the sphere of its repulsive force, and hence that aA is the radius of this sphere. Thus between a, where the penetration of an external monad into the space occupied by the sphere in question is resisted, and A, the center of the sphere, a point c can be specified (according to the infinite divisibility of space). Now, if A resists whatever endeavors to penetrate into a, then c must resist both the points A and a, for if this were not so, they would approach each other unimpeded; consequently, A and a would meet in the point c, i.e., the space would be penetrated. Therefore, there must be something in c that resists the penetration of A and a, and thus repels the monad A as much as this something is repelled by the monad. Now, since repulsion is a motion, c is something movable in space, i.e., matter; and the space between A and a could not be filled by the sphere of the activity of a single monad, neither could the space between c and A, and so on to infinity.

505

Mathematicians represent the repulsive forces of the parts of elastic matters in their greater or lesser compression as increasing or decreasing in a certain proportion to their distances from one another, e.g., the smallest parts of air repel each other in inverse proportion to their distances from one another because their elasticity stands in inverse proportion to the spaces within which they are compressed. One completely mistakes their meaning and misinterprets their language when he attributes to the object of the concept what necessarily belongs to the process of the construction of the concept. For according to this process, all contact can be represented as an infinitely small distance; moreover, this must necessarily happen in those cases where a larger or smaller space is to be represented as completely filled by the same quantity of matter, i.e., by one and the same quantum of repulsive forces. Consequently, as regards something infinitely divisible, there can be assumed no actual distance of parts, which always constitute a continuum as regards all expansion of the space of the whole, although the possibility of this expansion can be made intuitable only under the idea of an infinitely small distance.

Observation 2

Mathematics can indeed in its internal practice be quite indifferent with regard to the chicanery of a mistaken metaphysics and rest in the certain possession of its evident assertions of the infinite divisibility of space, regardless of what objections a sophistry picking over mere concepts may introduce against such divisibility. But in the application of its propositions valid for space to substance filling space, it must nevertheless concern itself with a test according to mere concepts, and hence with metaphysics. The above proposition is already a proof of this. For although matter is infinitely divisible from a mathematical point of view, it does not necessarily follow that matter is physically divisible to infinity, even if every part of space is again a space and consequently always includes within itself parts external to one another. For from this last fact one cannot prove that in every possible part of this filled space there is substance, and that, consequently, this substance, separated from everything else, exists as of itself movable. Therefore, something was lacking heretofore in the mathematical proof; without this something, such a proof could have no sure application
506 to natural science. This deficiency has been remedied in the proposition given above. But as for what concerns the remaining attacks of metaphysics upon the present physical proposition of the infinite divisibility of matter, the math-

ematician must cede these attacks entirely to the philosopher. The latter, moreover, by these objections, ventures
into a labyrinth out of which it becomes difficult for him to
find his way, even in questions immediately concerning him.
He thus has enough to do on his own account, without the
mathematician's being allowed to mix himself up in this
business. If, namely, matter is infinitely divisible, then (con-
cludes the dogmatic metaphysician) it consists of an infinite
multitude of parts; for a whole must in advance already contain within itself all the parts in their entirety into which it
can be divided. This last proposition is also indubitably certain of every whole as a thing in itself. Now, one cannot grant
that matter, or even space, consists of infinitely many parts
(because there is a contradiction involved in thinking of an
infinite number as complete, inasmuch as the concept of an
infinite number already implies that it can never be wholly
complete). Therefore, one must resolve either to defy the
geometer by saying that space is not divisible to infinity, or
to irritate the metaphysician by saying that space is no property of a thing in itself and hence that matter is not a thing
in itself but is the mere appearance of our external senses,
just as space is their essential form.

Here the philosopher now comes into the strait between
the horns of a dangerous dilemma. To deny the first proposition, that space is divisible to infinity, is an empty undertaking;
for mathematics does not admit of being reasoned away.
But yet to regard matter as a thing in itself and hence space
as a property of things in themselves is identical with denying
this first proposition. The philosopher sees himself thus
forced to depart from the assertion that matter is a thing
in itself and space a property of things in themselves, however common and suited to the common understanding this
assertion may be. But of course he departs from this assertion
only under the condition that in the event of his making
matter and space appearances only (hence making space
only the form of our external sensible intuition, and thus

making both matter and space not things in themselves but only subjective modes of representation of objects in themselves unknown to us), he is then helped out of the difficulty of matter's being infinitely divisible while yet not consisting of infinitely many parts. That matter consists of infinitely many parts can indeed be thought by reason, even though this thought cannot be constructed and rendered intuitable. For with regard to what is actual only by its being given in representation, there is not more given than is met with in the representation, i.e., as far as the progression of the representations reaches. Therefore, one can only say of appearances, whose division goes on to infinity, that there are

507   as many parts of the appearance as we give, i.e., as far as we want to divide. For the parts insofar as they belong to the existence of an appearance exist only in thought, namely, in the division itself. Now, the division indeed goes on to infinity, but it is never given as infinite; and hence it does not follow that the divisible contains within itself an infinite number of parts in themselves, that are outside of our representation, merely because the division goes on to infinity. For it is not the division of the thing but only the division of its representation that can be infinitely continued. Any division of the object (which is in itself unknown) can never be completed and hence can never be entirely given. Therefore, any division of the representation proves no actual infinite multitude to be in the object (since such a multitude would be an express contradiction). A great man[32] who perhaps contributes more than anyone else to maintain the reputation of mathematics in Germany has several times repulsed metaphysical presumptions of overturning the propositions of geometry concerning the infinite divisibility of space by the established reminder that space belongs only to the appearance of external things; but he has not been understood.

[32] [Alois Höfler, editor of the Akademie edition of the *Metaphysical Foundations of Natural Science,* suggests that Kant might mean either Leibniz, Wolff, Euler, Lambert, or Kästner.]

This proposition was taken as though he wanted to say that space appears to us, but otherwise it is a thing in itself or is a relation of things in themselves, and the mathematician considers it only as it appears. Instead of this he should have been understood as wanting to say that space is no property appertaining to anything outside of our senses, but is only the subjective form of our sensibility. Under this form objects of our external senses appear to us, but we do not know them as they are constituted in themselves. We call this appearance matter. By the foregoing misinterpretation space was always thought of as a quality adhering to things even outside of our power of representation, but the mathematician thought of this quality only according to common concepts, i.e., confusedly (for appearance is commonly explained in this way). By this same foregoing misinterpretation one attributed the mathematical proposition of the infinite divisibility of matter, a proposition presupposing the highest clarity in the concept of space, to a confused representation of space, which the geometer laid as his foundation. In this way it remained open to the metaphysician to compound space of points and matter of simple parts and thus (according to his opinion) to bring clarity into this concept of space. The ground of this aberration lies in a badly understood monadology, which does not at all belong to the explication of natural appearances but is a platonic concept of the world carried out by Leibniz. This concept is correct in itself insofar as the world is regarded not as an object of the senses but as a thing in itself, i.e., as merely an object of the understanding which nevertheless lies at the basis of the appearances of the senses. Now, the composite of things in themselves must certainly consist of the simple; for the parts must here be given before all composition. But the composite in the appearance does not consist of the simple, because in the appearance, which can never be given   *508* otherwise than as composite (extended), the parts can be given only through division and thus not before the com-

pulsive one, would be held within no limits of extension, i.e., would disperse itself to infinity, and no assignable quantity of matter would be found in any assignable space. Consequently, with merely repulsive forces of matter, all spaces would be empty; and hence, strictly speaking, there would be no matter at all. Therefore, forces which are opposed to the extensive ones, i.e., compressive forces, are required for the existence of all matter. But these cannot in turn be sought for originally in the opposition of another matter, for this other itself requires a compressive force in order that it may be matter. Consequently, there must be assumed an original force of matter acting in an opposite direction to the repulsive, and hence acting for approach, i.e., an attractive force. Now, inasmuch as this attractive force belongs to the possibility of matter as matter in general, and consequently precedes all distinctions of matter; so this force must not be attributed merely to a particular species of matter, but to every matter generally and originally. Thus an original attraction belongs to all matter as a fundamental force appertaining to its essence.

509

Observation

Regarding the transition from one property of matter to another property specifically different from it, and yet equally belonging to the concept of matter, even though not contained in this concept, the attitude of our understanding must be more closely considered. If attractive force is itself originally requisite for the possibility of matter, why do we not equally make use of it with impenetrability as the primary sign of matter? Why is impenetrability given immediately with the concept of matter, while attraction is not thought in the concept but only attributed to it by inference? The fact that our senses do not let us perceive attraction so immediately as repulsion and the resistance of impenetrability cannot sufficiently answer the difficulty. For if we had

such a capacity, it is easy to comprehend that our understanding would nevertheless choose the filling of space in
order to designate thereby substance in space, i.e., matter,
just as in this filling of space, or, as it is otherwise called,
solidity, there is posited the characteristic of matter as a thing
distinct from space. Attraction, however well we might perceive it, would never reveal to us a matter of determinate
volume and shape, nor anything beyond the endeavor of our
perceiving organ to approach a point outside us (the central
point of the attracting body). For the attractive force of all
parts of the earth can affect us neither more nor otherwise
than if it were concentrated entirely in the center of the
earth and this point alone were what influenced our sense;
similarly with the attraction of a mountain, or of every stone,
etc. Now, we thereby obtain no determinate concept of any
object in space, since neither figure nor size nor even the
510   place where the object might be located can fall within the
range of our senses. (The mere direction of the attraction
would be able to be perceived, as in the case of weight; the
attracting point would be unknown, and I do not even see
how this point should be disclosed through inferences, without the perception of matter insofar as it fills space.) Thus
it is clear that the first application of our concepts of quantity to matter whereby there first becomes possible for us
the transformation of our external perceptions into the experiential concept of matter as object in general is founded
only on matter's property of filling space. By means of the
sense of feeling, this property provides us with the size and
shape of an extended thing, and hence with the concept of a
determinate object in space; this concept is laid at the foundation of all else that can be said about this thing. This is
doubtless the reason why, in spite of the clearest proofs that
attraction must belong to the fundamental forces of matter
equally as much as repulsion does, one nevertheless opposes
the former force so much, and wants to grant no other
forces at all besides those of impact and pressure (both by

means of impenetrability). For that whereby space is filled is substance, one says, and this is correct enough. But this substance reveals its existence to us by sense, whereby we perceive its impenetrability, namely, by feeling; hence it reveals its existence only in relation to contact, whose beginning (in the approach of one matter to another) is called impact, but whose continuation is called pressure. Because of this it seems as though the immediate action of one matter on another could never be anything else but pressure or impact, the only two influences we can immediately perceive; on the other hand, attraction, which in itself can give us either no sensation at all or at least no determinate object of sensation, is so difficult for us to think of as a fundamental force.

PROPOSITION 6

By mere attraction, without repulsion, no matter is possible.

Proof

Attractive force is that moving force of matter whereby it compels another to approach it; consequently, when such force is found among all parts of matter, then it endeavors by means of this force to diminish the distance of its parts from one another, and hence the space which they together occupy. Now, nothing can hinder the action of a moving force *511* except another moving force opposed to it; but the force that is opposed to attraction is repulsive force. Therefore, by mere approach, and without repulsive forces, all parts of matter would approach one another without hindrance and diminish the space that matter occupies. Since, now, in the case assumed there is no distance of parts with regard to which a greater approach through attraction would be made impossible by means of repulsive force, the parts would move toward one another until no distance between them would be found, i.e., they would coalesce in a mathematical point and the space would be empty and hence without any matter. Accordingly, matter is impossible by mere attractive forces without repulsive ones.

Note

That property upon which as a condition even the inner possibility of a thing rests is an essential element of its inner possibility. Therefore, repulsive force belongs just as much to the essence of matter as attractive force; and one cannot be separated from the other in the concept of matter.

Observation

Since one can think of no more than two moving forces in space, repulsion and attraction, it was previously necessary—so as to prove a priori the union of both in the concept of a matter in general—to consider each separately, in order to see what taken singly they could provide for the presentation of matter. It turns out, now, that whether one posits neither of them or assumes merely one, space always remains empty and no matter is found in it.

EXPLICATION 6

Contact in the physical sense is the immediate action and reaction of impenetrability. The action of one matter upon another outside of contact is action at a distance (*actio in distans*). This action at a distance, which is also possible without 512 out the mediation of matter lying in between, is called immediate action at a distance, or the action of matters on one another through empty space.

Observation

Contact in the mathematical meaning is the common bound-ary of two spaces and hence is within neither the one space nor the other. Therefore, straight lines cannot touch one another; but when they have a point in common, it belongs as much to the one as to the other of these lines when they are extended, i.e., they cut each other. But circle and straight line, circle and circle touch each other in a point, planes in a line, and bodies in planes. Mathematical contact lies at the basis of the physical but does not alone constitute it. In order that physical contact may arise from the mathe-matical, there must be thought in addition a dynamical rela-tion—and indeed not a dynamical one of the attractive forces but of the repulsive ones, i.e., of impenetrability. Physical contact is the reciprocal action of repulsive forces at the common boundary of two matters.

PROPOSITION 7

The attraction essential to all matter is an immediate action through empty space of one matter upon another.

Proof

The original attractive force itself contains the ground of the possibility of matter as that thing which fills a space in a de-terminate degree, and hence contains the ground of the very possibility of a physical contact of matter. Therefore, this attractive force must precede the physical contact of matter; and its action must, consequently, be independent of the condition of contact. Now, the action of a moving force that is independent of all contact is also independent of the filling of space between the moving thing and the thing moved, i.e., such action must take place without the space between the moving thing and the thing moved being filled, and hence takes place as action through empty space. Therefore, the original and essential attraction of all matter is an immediate action of one matter upon another through empty space.

513   ## Observation 1

That the possibility of fundamental forces should be made conceivable is a completely impossible demand; for they are called fundamental forces precisely because they cannot be derived from any other force, i.e., they cannot be conceived.[33] But the original attractive force is not the least bit more inconceivable than the original repulsion. The original attractive force merely does not offer itself so immediately to the senses as impenetrability does in furnishing us concepts of determinate objects in space. Inasmuch as attraction is not felt but is only to be inferred, it therefore appears to be a derived force, just as though it were only a hidden play of moving forces produced by repulsion. Considering attraction more closely, we see that it cannot be further derived from any source, least of all from the moving force of matters through their impenetrability, since its action is just the opposite of impenetrability. The most common objection to immediate action at a distance is that a matter cannot directly act where it is not. When the earth directly influences the moon to approach it, it acts upon a thing many thousand miles removed from it, but nevertheless acts immediately; the

[33] [By "conceive" Kant here means to derive a concept (or concepts) from more fundamental ones. Those which cannot be derived from any others cannot be conceived but only assumed for one reason or another (for example, the concept of substance is an a priori category, whose possibility requires a transcendental deduction, or justification; we are made aware of repulsive force through the sensation of resistance, etc.). And so the possibility of matter in general as something possessing a definite degree of the filling of space can be conceived by deriving matter from the fundamental forces of repulsion and attraction, whose possibility cannot be conceived. See below, Ak. 524–525, 534.]

space between it and the moon may be regarded as entirely empty, for although matter may lie between both bodies, this fact does not affect the attraction. Therefore, attraction acts directly in a place where it is not—something that seems to be contradictory. But it is so far from being contradictory that one can say, rather, that everything in space acts on another only in a place where the acting thing is not. For if the thing should act in the same place where it is itself, then the thing upon which it acts would not be outside it; for "outside" means presence in a place where the other thing is not. If earth and moon touched each other, the point of contact would be a place where neither the earth nor the moon is; for both are removed from one another by the sum of their radii. Moreover, no part either of the earth or of the moon would be found at the point of contact; for this point lies at the boundary of both filled spaces, and this boundary constitutes no part either of the one or of the other. That matters, therefore, cannot immediately act on each other at a distance would be tantamount to saying that they cannot immediately act on each other without the intervention of the forces of impenetrability. Now, this would be tantamount to my saying that repulsive forces are the only ones by which matters can be active or are at least the necessary conditions under which alone matters can act upon one another. This would declare the force of attraction to be either wholly impossible or always dependent on the action of repulsive forces, but both are assertions without any foundation. The confusion of the mathematical contact of spaces 514 and the physical contact through repulsive forces constitutes the ground of the misunderstanding here. To attract immediately outside of contact means to approach one another according to a constant law without the repulsive force's containing the condition of such approach; this must admit of being thought of, just as well as to repel one another immediately, i.e., to fly from one another according to a constant law without the attractive force's having any share therein. For both moving forces are wholly different in kind, and there is not the least foundation for making one dependent on the other and claiming that one is not possible without the intervention of the other.

Observation 2

No motion at all can arise from attraction in contact; for contact is the reciprocal action of impenetrability, which impedes all motion. There must, consequently, be some immediate attraction outside of contact, and hence at a distance; for otherwise even the forces of pressure and impact, which are to produce the endeavor to approach, could have no cause, or at least no cause lying originally in the nature of matter, inasmuch as they act with the repulsive force of matter in the opposite direction [to attraction]. One may call that attraction which occurs without the intervention of repulsive forces the true attraction, and that which proceeds merely in the other manner the apparent; for, strictly speaking, the body that another is striving merely in this latter way to approach exercises no attractive force whatever on this other body, because this other has been driven toward the first body from elsewhere by impact. But even these apparent attractions must nevertheless ultimately have a true one at their basis, because matter, whose pressure or impact is to serve instead of attraction, would not even be matter without attractive forces (Proposition 5); consequently, the mode of explicating all phenomena of approach by merely apparent attraction moves in a circle. It is commonly held that Newton did not find it necessary for his system to assume an immediate attraction of matters, but with the strictest abstinence of pure mathematics herein left the physicists full freedom to explain the possibility of such attraction as they might find good, without mixing up his propositions with their play of hypotheses. But how could he establish the proposition that the universal attraction of bodies, which they exercise equi-

distantly on all sides, is proportional to the quantity of their matter, if he did not assume that all matter exercises this motive force simply as matter and by its essential nature? For certainly in the case of two bodies, whether homogeneous or not as to matter, if one pulls the other, the mutual approach (according to the law of the equality of reciprocal action) must always occur in inverse proportion to the quantity of   515
the matter. Nevertheless, this law constitutes only a principle of mechanics, not of dynamics, i.e., it is a law of motions following from attractive forces but not of the proportion of attractive forces themselves, and this law is valid for all moving forces in general. Therefore, if a magnet is at one time attracted by another identically similar magnet, and at another time is attracted by this same other magnet enclosed in a wooden box that is double this second magnet's weight, then in the latter case this second magnet will impart more relative motion to the first magnet than in the former case, although the wood, which increases the quantity of the matter of this second magnet, adds nothing at all to its attractive force and manifests no magnetic attraction of the box. Newton says (Cor. 2, Prop. 6, Lib. III, *Princip. Phil. N.*): "If the ether or any other body were without weight, it would, inasmuch as it differs from any other matter in nothing but form, be able to be transformed little by little through a gradual change of this form into a matter of the kind that has the greatest weight on earth; and, conversely, this latter by a gradual change of its form would be able to lose all its weight, which is contrary to experience, etc."[34] Thus he did

[34] [Kant has rendered Newton rather freely. Newton says, "If the ether, or any other body, were either altogether void of gravity or were to gravitate less in proportion to its quantity of matter, then, because (according to Aristotle, Descartes, and others) there is no difference between that and other bodies but in mere form of matter, by a successive change from form to form, it might be changed at last into a body of the same condition with those which gravitate most in proportion of their quantity of matter; and, on the other hand, the heaviest bodies, acquiring the first form of that body, might by degrees quite lose their gravity. And therefore the weights

not even exclude the ether (much less other matters) from the law of attraction. What kind of matter, then, could remain for him, by whose impact the approach of bodies to one another could be regarded as mere apparent attraction? Therefore, if we take the liberty of substituting for the true attraction, which he asserted, an apparent one, and of assuming the necessity of an impulse through impact in order to explicate the phenomenon of approach; then we cannot cite this great founder of the theory of attraction as our precursor. He rightly abstracted from all hypotheses in answering the question regarding the cause of the universal attraction of matter; for this question is physical or metaphysical, but not mathematical. And although in the advertisement to the second edition of his *Optics* he says, *ne quis gravitatem inter essentiales corporum proprietates me habere · existimet, quaestionem unam de ejus causa investiganda subjeci*,[35] one can well note that the offense which his contemporaries and perhaps he himself took at the concept of an original attraction made him at variance with himself. For he absolutely could not say that the attractive forces of two planets, e.g., Jupiter and Saturn, which they manifest at equal distances of their satellites (whose mass is unknown), are proportional to the quantity of the matter of these heavenly bodies, unless he assumed that they merely as matter, and hence according to a universal property of the same, attracted other matter.

---

would depend upon the forms of bodies and, with those forms, might be changed, contrary to what was proved in the preceding Corollary." The preceding corollary says, "Hence the weights of bodies do not depend upon their forms and textures; for if the weights could be altered with the forms, they would be greater or less, according to the variety of forms, in equal matter, altogether against experience." *Mathematical Principles of Natural Philosophy*, Florian Cajori's revision of Andrew Motte's translation of 1729 (Berkeley and Los Angeles: University of California Press, 1962), Vol. II, pp. 413–414.]

[35] ["And to show that I do not take gravity for an essential property of bodies, I have added one question concerning its cause. . . ."]

EXPLICATION 7   *516*

A moving force by which matters can directly act on one another only at the common surface of contact, I call a superficial force; but that whereby one matter can directly act on the parts of another beyond the surface of contact, a penetrative force.

Note

Repulsive force, by means of which matter fills a space, is a mere superficial force. For the parts touching each other mutually limit each other's sphere of action; the repulsive force cannot move any more distant part except by means of those lying between, and an immediate action (passing right through these parts) of one matter upon another by means of the forces of extension is impossible. On the other hand, no intervening matter limits an attractive force. By means of such a force a matter occupies a space without filling it; thereby matter acts through empty space upon other distant matters, and no intervening matter limits the action of such a force. Now, it is thus that the original attraction, which makes matter itself possible, must be thought. Therefore, it is a penetrative force and for this reason alone is always proportional to the quantity of the matter.

PROPOSITION 8

The original attractive force, upon which the very possibility of matter as such rests, extends itself directly throughout the universe to infinity, from every part of the universe to every other part.

Proof

Because the original attractive force, namely, to act immediately at a distance, belongs to the essence of matter, it
also belongs to every part of matter. Now, let it be granted
517   that there is a distance beyond which the force of attraction
does not reach; this limitation of the sphere of its efficacy
would rest either on the matter lying within this sphere or
merely on the magnitude of the space in which its influence
is spread. The first does not take place, for this attraction is
a penetrative force and acts directly at a distance, in spite
of all intervening matters, through every space as an empty
space. The second likewise does not take place. For inasmuch
as every attraction is a moving force having a degree, beyond
which ever smaller degrees to infinity can be thought; in
the greater distance there would indeed lie a cause for
diminishing the degree of attraction in inverse proportion to
the amount of the diffusion of the force, but never for completely destroying it. Now, since there is hence nothing
which might anywhere limit the sphere of the efficacy of the
original attraction of any part of matter, this attraction
reaches out beyond all assignable limits to every other
matter, and hence reaches throughout the universe to
infinity.

Note 1

From this original attractive force as a penetrative force exercised by all matter upon all matter, and hence in proportion
to the quantity of matter and spreading its action throughout all possible regions—from this force, I say, in combination with its counteracting one, namely, repulsive force, the
limitation of this latter, and hence the possibility of a space
filled in a determinate degree, must admit of being derived.
And thus would the dynamical concept of matter as the movable filling its space (in a determinate degree) be constructed.

But for this construction one needs a law of the relation both of original attraction and of original repulsion at various distances of the matter and of its parts from one another. Since this relation rests solely on the difference of direction of both these forces (inasmuch as a point is driven either to approach others or to recede from them) and on the size of the space into which each of these forces diffuses itself at various distances, this law is a pure mathematical problem, with which metaphysics is no longer concerned. Metaphysics is not responsible if the attempt to construct matter in this way is not crowned with success. For metaphysics answers merely for the correctness of the elements of the construction that are granted our rational cognition; it does not an- *518* swer for the insufficiency and limits of our reason in the execution of the construction.

Note 2

Since all given matter must fill its space with a determinate degree of repulsive force in order to constitute a determinate material thing, only an original attraction in conflict with the original repulsion can make a determinate degree of the filling of space, i.e., matter, possible. Now, it may be that the attraction involved in this determinate degree of the filling of space arises from the individual attraction of the parts of the compressed matter among one another or arises from the union of this compressed matter with the attraction of all the matter of the world.

The original attraction is proportional to the quantity of matter and reaches to infinity. Therefore, the determinate degree of the filling of space by matter cannot in the end be brought about without matter's infinitely reaching attraction; such a determinate degree of the filling of space can then be imparted to every matter in accordance with the degree of its repulsive force.

The action of universal attraction, which all matter exercises directly on all matter and at all distances, is called gravitation; the endeavor to move in the direction of the greater gravitation is weight. The action of the universal repulsive force of the parts of every given matter is called its original elasticity. Therefore, this elasticity and the aforementioned weight constitute the only a priori comprehensible universal characteristics of matter, the former being internal, the latter involving an external relation; for the possibility of matter itself rests upon these two foundations. When cohesion is explained as the reciprocal attraction of matter insofar as this attraction is limited solely to the condition of contact, then such cohesion does not belong to the possibility of matter in general and cannot therefore be cognized a priori as bound up with matter. This property would hence not be metaphysical but physical, and therefore would not belong to our present considerations.

Observation 1

I cannot forbear adding a small preliminary observation for the sake of any attempt that may perhaps be made toward such a possible construction.

1. One may say of every force which directly acts at dif-
519   ferent distances and which is limited as to the degree whereby it exercises moving force upon any given point at a certain distance from it only by the size of the space in which it must diffuse itself in order to act upon that point— of such a force one may say that in all spaces through which it is diffused, however small or great they may be, it always constitutes an equal quantum, but that the degree of its action upon that point in this space always stands in inverse proportion to the space through which it has had to diffuse itself in order to be able to act upon that point. So, for instance, light diffuses itself everywhere from an illuminating point in spherical surfaces that ever increase with the square of the distance, and the quantity of the illumination in all

these infinitely larger spherical surfaces is as a whole always the same. Whence it follows that an equal part in any one of these spherical surfaces must according to degree be so much the less illuminated as the diffusion surface of the same quantity of light is greater. And so it is with all other forces and laws according to which these forces must diffuse themselves either into surfaces or corporeal space in order to act according to their nature upon distant objects. It is better to represent the diffusion of a moving force from one point to all distances in this manner than it is to represent this diffusion in the ordinary way, as such representation occurs (being one among other such ways) in optics, by means of rays diverging in a circle from a central point. For lines drawn in this way can never fill the space through which they pass, nor therefore the surface which they reach, regardless of how many of them are drawn or plotted; this is the inevitable consequence of their divergence. Thus they only give occasion to troublesome inferences, and these to hypotheses which could very well be avoided if one were to consider merely the size of the whole spherical surface which is to be uniformly illuminated by the same quantity of light, and if one took the degree of the illumination of the surface in any one place as inversely proportional to the size of the whole surface, as is natural; and similarly with every other diffusion of a force through spaces of different sizes.

2. If the force is an immediate attraction at a distance, the lines of the direction of the attraction must still less be represented as rays diverging from the attracting point, but, rather, must be represented as converging at the attracting point from all points of the surrounding spherical surface (whose radius is the given distance). For the line of direction of the motion to this point, which is the cause and goal of the motion, already assigns the *terminus a quo,* from which the lines must begin, namely, from all points of the surface. These lines have their direction from this *terminus* to the attracting center, and not vice versa. For only the size of the surface

sumed repelling point, even though the direction of the motion has this point for a *terminus a quo*. The reason for this lies in the fact that the space in which the force must be diffused in order to act at a distance is a corporeal space that is to be thought of as filled. The way in which a point can fill a space corporeally by moving force, i.e., dynamically, is certainly capable of no further mathematical presentation; and diverging rays coming from a point cannot possibly represent the repelling force of a corporeally filled space. Rather, one would estimate the repulsion at various infinitely small distances of these mutually repelling points simply in inverse proportion to the corporeal spaces that each of these points dynamically fills, and hence in inverse proportion to the cube of the distances of these points from one another, without one's being able to construct these points.

4. Therefore, the original attraction of matter would act in inverse proportion to the square of the distance at all distances and the original repulsion in inverse proportion to the cube of the infinitely small distances. By such an action and reaction of both fundamental forces, matter would be possible by a determinate degree of the filling of its space. For inasmuch as the repulsion increases in greater measure upon approach of the parts than the attraction does, the limit of approach beyond which by means of the given attraction no greater is possible is determined, and hence the degree of compression that constitutes the measure of the intensive filling of space is also determined.

Observation 2

I see well the difficulty of this mode of explicating the possibility of matter in general. This difficulty consists in the fact that if a point cannot directly drive another by repulsive force without at the same time filling the whole corporeal space up to the given distance by its force, then this space must, as seems to follow, contain several repulsive points.

This fact contradicts the assumption, but this fact was refuted above (Proposition 4) under the name of a sphere of repulsion of the simple in space. However, there is a distinction to be made between the concept of an actual space, which can be given, and the mere idea of a space, which is thought only for the determination of the relation of given spaces but which is in fact no space. In the case cited of a supposed physical monadology, there were to be actual spaces which were filled by a point dynamically, i.e., through repulsion; for they existed as points before any possible production of matter from these points, and they determined by the proper sphere of their activity that part of the space to be filled which could belong to them. Therefore, in the hypothesis in question, matter cannot be regarded as infinitely divisible and as continuous quantity; for the parts, which directly repel one another, have nevertheless a determinate distance from one another (the sum of the radii of the sphere of their repulsion). On the other hand, when we, as actually happens, think of matter as continuous quantity, no distance whatsoever of the directly mutually repelling parts obtains, and hence no increasing or decreasing spheres of their immediate activity. However, matters can expand or be compressed (like the air), and in this case one represents to himself a distance of their nearest parts, that can increase and decrease. But inasmuch as the closest parts of a continuous matter 522 touch one another, whether it is further expanded or compressed, one thinks of their distances from one another as infinitely small, and this infinitely small space as filled in a greater or lesser degree by their force of repulsion. The infinitely small intermediate space is, however, not at all different from contact. Hence it is only the idea of space that serves to render intuitable the expansion of matter as continuous quantity; whether this idea is indeed in this way actual cannot be conceived. When it is said, then, that the repulsive forces of the directly mutually driving parts of matter stand in inverse proportion to the cube of their distances, this means only that they stand in inverse proportion to the corporeal spaces which one thinks of between parts that nevertheless immediately touch each other, and whose distance must just for this reason be termed infinitely small in order that such distance may be distinguished from all actual distance. Hence one must not from the difficulties of the construction of a concept, or rather from the misinterpretation of the construction, raise any objection to the concept itself; for otherwise the concept would concern the mathematical presentation of the proportion with which attraction occurs at different distances, as well as those distances through which each point in an expanding or compressed whole of matter directly repels another point. The universal law of dynamics would in both cases be this: the action of the moving force that is exercised by one point upon every other one external to it is in inverse proportion to the space in which the same quantity of moving force has had to diffuse itself in order to act directly upon this other point at the determinate distance.

From the law that the parts of matter originally repel one another in inverse cubic proportion to their infinitely small distances, there must necessarily follow a law of the expansion and compression of these parts that is entirely different from the law of Mariotte[37] regarding the air. Mariotte's law proves that the forces causing the closest parts of the air to flee from one another stand in inverse proportion to the distances of the parts, as Newton proves (*Princ. Ph. N.*, Lib. II, Propos. 23, Schol.). But one cannot regard the expansive force of the parts of the air as the action of originally repulsive forces; for this expansive force rests on heat, which compels the proper parts of the air (to which, moreover, actual distances from each other may be conceded) to fly from one another, and acts not merely as a matter interpen-

<hr/>

[37] [Edme Mariotte (1620–1684) was a French physicist. The law named after him appeared in his treatise *Concerning the Nature of the Air* (1679).]

etrating the parts but, to all appearance, through its vibrations. But that these vibrations must impart to the air's parts
closest to one another a force that causes them to flee from
one another and that stands in inverse proportion to the distances of the parts can be made readily conceivable according to the laws of the communication of motion through the
vibration of elastic matters.

Yet I declare that I do not want the present exposition of
the law of an original repulsion to be regarded as necessarily
523   belonging to the aim of my metaphysical treatment of matter, nor do I want this treatment (for which it is enough to
have presented the filling of space as a dynamic property of
matter) to be mixed up with the disputes and doubts which
might befall this exposition.

GENERAL
NOTE
TO DYNAMICS

If we review all our discussions of the metaphysical treatment
of matter, we shall observe that in this treatment the following things have been taken into consideration: first, the *real*
in space (otherwise called the solid) in its filling of space
through repulsive force; second, that which, with regard to
the first as the proper object of our external perception, is
negative, namely, attractive force, by which, as far as may
be, all space would be penetrated, i.e., the solid would be
wholly abolished; third, the *limitation* of the first force by the
second and the consequent perceptible determination of the
degree of a filling of space. Hence we observe that the quality of matter has been completely dealt with under the
moments of reality, negation, and limitation,[38] as much as
such a treatment belongs to a metaphysical dynamics.

[38] [Cf. *Critique of Pure Reason,* B 106.]

GENERAL
OBSERVATION
ON DYNAMICS

The universal principle of the dynamics of material nature is this: all that is real in the objects of our external senses and is not merely a determination of space (place, extension, and figure) must be regarded as moving force. By this principle, therefore, the so-called solid, or absolute impenetrability, is banished from natural science as an empty concept, and in its stead repulsive force is posited. On the other hand, the true and immediate attraction is defended against all the sophistries of a metaphysics that misunderstands itself, and this attraction is explained as a fundamental force necessary even to the possibility of the concept of matter. From all this there arises the consequence that, should it be found necessary, space could be assumed to be at all events filled throughout and yet in varying degree, without distributing empty intermediate spaces within matter. For according to the originally varying degree of repulsive forces, upon which rests the first property of matter, namely, that of filling a space, the relationship of this property to original attraction (whether to the attraction of every matter of itself, or to the united attraction of all matter in the universe) can be thought *524* of as infinitely diverse. This is because attraction rests on the mass of matter in a given space, while the expansive force of matter rests on the degree to which the space is filled; this degree can be specifically very different (as the same quantity of air in the same volume exhibits more or less elasticity according to its greater or lesser heating). The general ground involved here is that by true attraction all parts of matter act directly on all parts of other matter; but by expansive force, only the parts in the surface of contact act, and thereby it is all the same whether behind this surface much or little of this matter is found. From all this a great advantage arises for natural science, by its being relieved of the burden of building a world merely according to fancy out of fulness and emptiness. Rather, all spaces can be thought of as full and yet as filled in varying measure. By means of this, empty space at least loses its necessity and is reduced to the value of a hypothesis, since otherwise it might claim the title of a principle, under the pretext of being a necessary condition for the explication of the different degrees of the filling of space.

In connection with all this, the advantage of a methodically employed metaphysics to the detriment of principles that are also metaphysical but have not been brought to the test of criticism [Kritik] is apparently only negative. Nevertheless, indirectly the field of the investigator of nature is enlarged, because the conditions by which he previously limited his field and by which all original moving forces were philosophized away now lose their validity. But one must guard against going beyond what makes the universal concept of matter in general possible and against wanting to explain a priori the particular or even specific determination and variety of matter. The concept of matter is reduced to nothing but moving forces; this could not be expected to be otherwise, because in space no activity and no change can be thought of but mere motion. But who claims to comprehend the possibility of fundamental forces? They can only be assumed, if they inevitably belong to a concept concerning which there can be proved that it is a fundamental concept not further derivable from any other (such as is the fundamental concept of the filling of space).[39] These fundamental

[39] [This is to say that we can comprehend a priori the possibility of matter in general as composed of the two fundamental moving forces (as the foregoing part of dynamics has shown), but we cannot comprehend a priori the possibility of these original forces themselves nor can we explain a priori the specific varieties of matter as they are composed of various combinations of these forces. Compare below, Ak. 534: "Besides the ether, no law whatever of attractive or of repulsive force may be risked on a priori conjectures; but everything, even universal attraction as the cause of gravity, must, together

forces are the repulsive forces in general and the attractive forces in general (which counteract the repulsive ones). We can indeed judge well enough a priori concerning their connection and consequences; one may think of whatever relations of these forces among one another he wants to, provided he does not contradict himself. But he must not, therefore, presume to assume either of them as actual, because the authorization to set up a hypothesis irremissibly requires that the possibility of what is assumed be entirely certain. But in the case of fundamental forces, their possibility can never be comprehended. And because of this fact the mathematico-mechanical mode of explication has over the metaphysico-dynamical mode an advantage that the latter cannot provide, namely, from a completely homogeneous material, by means of the manifold shape of the parts, with empty intermediate spaces interspersed, this mathematico-mechanical mode can accomplish a great specific multiplicity of matters, according to their density as well as their mode of action (if foreign forces be superadded). For the possibility of the shapes as well as of the empty intermediate spaces can be proved with mathematical evidence. On the other hand, if the material itself is transformed into fundamental forces (whose laws we are not able to determine a priori, but still less are we able to reliably indicate a manifold of such forces sufficient for explicating the specific variety of matter), then all means are wanting for the construction of this concept

525

with the laws of such attraction, be concluded from data of experience. Still less will such conclusions in regard to chemical affinities be permitted to be tried otherwise than by means of experiment. For to comprehend original forces a priori according to their possibility lies generally beyond the horizon of our reason. Rather, all natural philosophy consists in the reduction of given forces apparently diverse to a smaller number of forces and powers sufficient for the explication of the actions of the former. But this reduction continues only to fundamental forces, beyond which our reason cannot go." However, in the *Transition from the Metaphysical Foundations of Natural Science to Physics* Kant explored these problems further, and claimed there that more can be comprehended a priori than he thought was possible here in the *Metaphysical Foundations of Natural Science.*]

and for presenting as possible in intuition what we thought universally. But a merely mathematical physics pays for the foregoing advantage doubly on the other side, in that it first of all must lay at its foundation an empty concept (that of absolute impenetrability), and secondly must give up all the proper forces of matter. In addition, with its original configurations of the fundamental material and its interspersion of empty spaces, it is afterwards required to make explications and must then allow the imagination more freedom in the field of philosophy—and indeed allow this freedom as a rightful claim—than can be consistent with the caution of philosophy.

I am unable to furnish an adequate explication of the possibility of matter and its specific variety from the fundamental forces; instead I shall, as I hope, completely present the moments to which its specific variety must all together admit of being reduced a priori (although I cannot conceive the possibility in the same way). The observations inserted between the definitions will elucidate the application of these definitions.

1. A *body,* in the physical signification, is a matter between determinate boundaries (and such matter therefore has a figure). The space between these boundaries, considered according to its magnitude, is the body's *content of space* (*volumen*). The degree of the filling of a space of determinate content is called *density.* (Otherwise the expression "dense" is also used absolutely for what is not·hollow—vesicular, porous.) In this sense there is an absolute density in the system of absolute impenetrability, namely, if a matter contains no empty intermediate spaces at all. According to this concept of the filling of space one draws comparisons and calls one matter containing less emptiness within itself denser than another, until finally that matter no part of whose space is empty is termed perfectly dense. One can make use of the latter expression only in accordance with the merely mathematical concept of matter. But in the dynamical system of a merely

relative impenetrability there is no maximum or minimum of density, and any matter however thin can equally be called fully dense if it entirely fills its space without containing 526 empty intermediate spaces, i.e., if it is a continuum and not an interruptum. But it is less dense, in the dynamical sense, in comparison with another matter if it entirely fills its space but not in an equal degree. However, even in the dynamical system it is unsuitable to think of a relation of matters according to their density unless they are represented as specifically homogeneous among one another, so that one can be produced from the other by mere compression. Now, since this last condition does not appear to be necessarily requisite to the nature of all matter in itself, no comparison can properly be permitted between heterogeneous matters with regard to their density, e.g., between water and quicksilver, although this is customary.

2. Attraction, insofar as it is thought as active merely in contact, is called *cohesion*. (Indeed one proves by very good experiments that the same force which in contact is called cohesion is found to be active also at a very small distance. But attraction is only called cohesion insofar as I think of it merely in contact, in accordance with common experience; with regard to such experience, attraction is scarcely perceived at small distances. Cohesion is commonly assumed to be an altogether universal property of matter, not as if one were led to this property already through the concept of matter, but because experience presents it everywhere. But this universality must not be understood collectively, as though every matter through this kind of attraction acted simultaneously upon every other matter in the universe—in the same way as gravitation—but merely disjunctively, namely, as though every matter through this kind of attraction acted upon one matter or another, of whatever kind these might be, that come in contact with it. Now, this attraction, as is provable on various grounds, is not a penetrating force but only a superficial one, inasmuch as it is not itself

as such determined everywhere according to density. For complete strength of cohesion one needs a preceding state of fluidity of the matters together with a subsequent solidification of them; and the closest fitting contact of broken but hard matters in the same surfaces in which they previously firmly cohered, e.g., a looking-glass where there is a crack, does not any way nearly admit the degree of attraction that these matters had from their solidification after being fluid. For all these reasons I hold this attraction in contact to be no fundamental force of matter, but to be only a derivative one. But more of this later.) A matter whose parts, notwithstanding their strong cohesion among one another, can yet be displaced past one another by every moving force, however small, is *fluid.* But parts of a matter are *displaced* past one another if, without diminishing the amount of contact, they are merely compelled to change their parts among
527   themselves. Parts, and hence matters too, are *separated* if their contact with others is not merely changed, but is destroyed, or the amount of contact is diminished. A *solid*—better, a *rigid*—body (*corpus rigidum*) is one whose parts cannot be displaced past one another by any force; these parts, consequently, resist displacement with a certain degree of force. The hindrance to the displacement of matters past one another is *friction.* The resistance to separation of matters in contact is cohesion. Fluid matters, therefore, undergo no friction in their division; but where friction is found, the matters are assumed, at least in their smaller parts, to be rigid —in greater or lesser degree, the lesser being called viscosity (*viscositas*). The rigid body is *brittle* if its parts cannot be displaced past one another without breaking, and hence if the cohesion of the parts cannot be changed without this cohesion's being at the same time destroyed. The difference between fluid and solid matters is very incorrectly placed in the different degree of the cohesion of their parts. For to call a matter fluid does not depend on the degree of its resistance

to rupture, but only on that of its resistance to the displacement of its parts past one another. The former can be as great
as one wants; the latter is always in a fluid matter $= 0$. Let us
consider a drop of water. If a particle within the drop is
drawn to one side by an ever so great attraction of the neigh-
boring parts touching it, then it will be drawn just as much
to the opposite side. And since the attractions mutually
cancel their actions, the particle is just as easily movable as
if it were in empty space, namely, the force that is to move
it has no cohesion to overcome, but only the so-called inertia, which it would have to overcome in the case of all
matter, even if the matter did not cohere at all. Therefore, a
small microscopic animacule will move as easily within this
drop as if there were no cohesion at all to separate. For it
does not really have any cohesion of the water to destroy;
nor any contact of the water within itself to diminish, but
only to change. But think of this animacule as wanting to
work its way through the outer surface of the drop. There
is first to be noted the fact that the mutual attraction of the
parts of this drop of water cause them to move themselves
until they have arrived at the greatest contact among one
another, and hence at the smallest contact with empty
space, i.e., until they have constituted a globular shape. Now,
if the said insect is trying to work its way beyond the surface
of the drop, then it must change this globular shape and
consequently bring about more contact of the water with the
empty space and hence less contact of the parts of the water
among one another, i.e., diminish their cohesion. And here   *528*
the water for the first time resists the insect by its cohesion,
but not by any cohesion within the drop, where the contact
of the parts among one another is not at all lessened but only
changed in their contact with other parts, i.e., they are
not in the least separated but only displaced. Moreover, one
may apply to the microscopic animacule what Newton says
about the light ray, and indeed for similar reasons: that it

capillary). If one supposes both arms to be a few hundred feet high, then the fluid matter in the narrow arm would stand just as high as that in the wide, according to the laws of hydrostatics. But the pressure on the bottom of the tubes and hence also on the part joining both tubes (which stand in communication) can be thought of as ever greater to infinity in proportion to the heights. Because of this, if the least friction among the parts of the fluid took place, then one should be able to find a height of the tubes with regard to which a small quantity of water poured into the narrower tube would not displace the water in the wider tube from its position, and hence the column of water in the narrower tube would come to stand higher than that in the wider inasmuch as the lower parts in the narrower, with such great   *529* pressure against one another, would no longer admit of displacement by means of so small a moving force as is provided by the added weight of the water. But this is contrary to experience and even to the concept of what is fluid. The same thing holds if instead of pressure by weight, the cohesion of the parts is posited, and the latter may be as great as one wants. The second definition of fluidity cited,[41] upon which the fundamental law of hydrostatics rests, says that fluidity is the property of a matter inasmuch as every part of the matter endeavors to move itself toward all sides with just the same force with which it is pressed in a given direction. This second definition follows from the first one[42] if there is combined with the first the fundamental principle of general dynamics. This principle says that all matter is originally elastic since it must endeavor to extend itself—i.e. (if the parts of a matter admit of being displaced without hindrance past one another by any force, as is actually the case with fluid matter) it must endeavor to move itself

[41] [Cf. above, Ak. 528.]

[42] [Cf. above, Ak. 526 ad fin.]

toward all sides of the space in which it is compressed with the same force with which the pressure in any given direction, whatever it may be, occurs. Therefore, it is only to rigid matters (whose possibility requires another ground of explication than that of the cohesion of parts) that one can, properly speaking, attribute friction; and friction already presupposes the property of rigidity. But certain matters, although they perhaps have a greater, or even a smaller force of cohesion than other fluid matters have, nevertheless very strongly resist displacement of their parts and therefore do not admit of separation otherwise than by the destruction of the cohesion of all parts in a given surface, thus giving the illusion of a superior cohesion. But why this is so, and hence how rigid bodies are possible, is still an unsolved problem, in spite of the ease with which ordinary natural science believes itself to dispose of it.

3. *Elasticity* (spring force) is the capacity of a matter to reassume its size or shape altered by another moving force when such a force has ceased. It is either expansive or attractive elasticity, the former in order after compression to assume the previously greater volume, the latter in order after expansion to assume the previously smaller volume. (Attractive elasticity, as the expression itself shows, is obviously derivative. An iron wire stretched by an appended weight springs back into its original volume when the connection is cut. In virtue of this attraction, which is the cause of the cohesion of the wire, or in the case of fluid matters, as when the heat is suddenly withdrawn from quicksilver, their matter would hasten to reassume the previously smaller volume. The elasticity which consists only in the recovery of the previous figure is always attractive, as in the case of a bent sword blade in which the parts on the convex surface, which are pulled away from one another, endeavor to assume their former proximity; and in the same way a small drop of quick-
530   silver may be called elastic. But expansive elasticity may be original or it may be derivative. Thus the air has a derivative

elasticity by means of the heat's matter[43] that is most inti-
mately united with it and whose elasticity is perhaps original.
On the other hand, the fundamental material of the fluid
which we call air must nevertheless, as matter in general,
already have in itself elasticity that is called original. It is impossible to decide with certainty as to what kind a perceived elasticity may be in cases that present themselves.)

4. The action of moved bodies on one another through
the communication of their motion is called *mechanical;*
but the action of matters at rest insofar as they change the
combination of their parts reciprocally by their own forces is
called *chemical.* This chemical influence is called *solution*
insofar as this influence has for its effect the separation of
the parts of a matter (mechanical division, e.g., that by means
of a wedge driven between the parts of a matter, is thus
entirely different from chemical division, because the wedge
does not act by its own force); but the influence that has for
its effect the dissociation of two matters dissolved in one
another is chemical *analysis.* The solution of specifically different matters in one another in which no part of one matter is found not united with a part of the other matter in the
same proportion as that of the whole solution is absolute
solution, and may also be called chemical penetration.
Whether the dissolving forces that are actually to be found
in nature are capable of effecting a complete solution may
remain undecided. Here the question is only whether such
a solution can be thought of. Now, it is obvious that as long as
the parts of a dissolved matter are still particles (*moleculae*),
a solution of them is not less possible than the solution of
the larger parts. Indeed it is obvious that this solution, if the
dissolving force continues, really must proceed until there is
no part left that is not composed of the solvent and the
matter to be dissolved in the proportion in which they each

---

[43] [Before the science of thermodynamics was developed in the nineteenth
century, many thought that heat phenomena could be accounted for by
positing the existence of a heat fluid, or caloric.]

stand to one another in the solution as a whole. Since, then, in such a case there can be no part of the volume of the solution that does not contain a part of the solvent, this solvent as a continuum must completely fill the volume. In the same way, since there can be no part of this volume of solution that does not contain a proportional part of the dissolved matter, this dissolved matter as a continuum must also fill the whole space constituting the volume of the mixture. But when two matters, and indeed each one of them, entirely fill one and the same space, they penetrate one another. Therefore, a perfect chemical solution would be a penetration of the matters. This chemical penetration would, nevertheless, be entirely different from the mechanical, since with regard to the latter one thinks that upon the closer approach of moved matters the repulsive force of the one could entirely outweigh that of the other, and one or both of these

531   forces could reduce the extension of these matters to nothing. On the other hand, in the case of chemical penetration the extension remains, but here the matters are not outside one another but within one another, i.e., by intussusception (as it is usually called) they together occupy a space proportional to the sum of their densities. It is difficult to oppose anything to the possibility of this perfect solution, and hence of chemical penetration, although such a solution does involve a complete division to infinity. Such a division, however, does not in this case contain any contradiction, because the solution takes place continuously throughout a time, i.e., through an infinite series of moments with acceleration. Moreover, by the division, the sums of the surfaces of the matters yet to be divided increase; and since the dissolving force acts continuously, the whole solution can be completed in a specifiable time. The inconceivability of such a chemical penetration of two matters is to be ascribed to the inconceivability of the divisibility to infinity of every continuum in general. If one departs from this complete solution, then one must assume the solution to extend only to

certain small particles of the matter to be dissolved, which swim in the solvent at fixed distances from one another, without one's being able to specify the least ground as to why these particles, since they are still divisible matters, are not also dissolved. For that the solvent does not act further may always be true enough in nature, as far as experience reaches. But the question here is about the possibility of a dissolving force that dissolves this particle and every other still remaining until the solution is completed. The volume occupied by the solution can be equal to the sum of the spaces occupied by the mutually dissolving matters before the mixture, or it can be smaller than this sum, or even larger than it, according to the way the attractive forces stand in relation to the repulsions. These mutually dissolving matters constitute in solution, each of itself and both combined, an elastic medium. This medium alone can provide a sufficient reason why the dissolved matter does not by its weight dissociate itself again from the solvent. For the latter's attraction, since it occurs equally strongly toward all sides, destroys the former's resistance. And to assume a certain viscosity in the fluid does not accord with the great force exercised by such fluids upon dissolved matters, e.g., acids diluted with water upon metallic bodies. Such bodies do not merely touch the acids, as must happen if they merely swam in their medium, but the acids with great attractive force separate these bodies from one another and disperse them throughout the entire space of the vehicle. Moreover, in case art [applied science, technical skill] might have in its power no chemical forces of solution of this kind to bring about a complete solution, nevertheless nature could perhaps exhibit such forces in its vegetal and animal operations and thereby could perhaps produce matters which, though indeed mixed, cannot be separated again by art. This 532 chemical penetration might even be found where one of the two matters is not separated by the other and in a literal sense dissolved, as, for instance, heat-matter [*Wärmestoff*] upon its figure is called a machine. The mode of explication of the specific variety of matters by the nature and composition of their smallest parts as machines is the mechanical natural philosophy. But that mode of explication which derives the specific variety of matter not from matters as machines, i.e., as mere tools of external moving forces, but from the proper moving forces of attraction and repulsion originally belonging to these matters may be called the dynamical natural philosophy. The mechanical mode of explication, since it is very convenient for mathematics, has, *533* under the name of the atomistic or corpuscular philosophy, always maintained its authority and influence on the principles of natural science with little change from old Democritus to Descartes and even to our own times. Its essentials consist in the assumption of the absolute impenetrability of the primitive matter, in the absolute homogeneity of this matter, differences only being allowed in the shape, and in the absolute unconquerability of the cohesion of the matter in these fundamental particles themselves. Such were the materials for the production of specifically different matters in order not only to have at hand an unchangeable and yet variously shaped fundamental matter for the unchangeability of species and kinds, but also to explain mechanically nature's various actions as arising from the shape of these primary parts as machines (to which nothing more was wanting than an externally impressed force). The first and foremost credential of this system rests, however, on the ostensibly unavoidable necessity of employing empty spaces for the specific distinction of the density of matters; these spaces were assumed to be distributed within the matters and among the aforementioned particles in a proportion, as was found necessary for the sake of some appearances, even so large that the filled part of the volume (even of the densest matter) would be very nearly nothing as compared with the empty part. In order, now, to introduce a dynamical mode of explication (which is far more suited and more favorable to experimental philosophy inasmuch as it leads directly to the discovery of the moving forces proper to matters and the laws of such forces, but restricts the freedom of assuming empty intermediate spaces and fundamental particles of determinate shapes, neither of which can be discovered and determined by any experiment), it is not at all necessary to forge new hypotheses, but only necessary to refute the postulate of the merely mechanical mode of explication, namely, that it is impossible to think of a specific difference of the density of matters without the intermixture of empty spaces. One can refute this postulate by merely citing a way in which this specific difference of the density of matters can be thought of without contradiction. For if this postulate, upon which the merely mechanical mode of explication stands, were only first declared invalid as a fundamental principle, then it is obvious that this postulate must not be adopted as a hypothesis in natural science as long as there remains a possibility of thinking of the specific difference of densities without any intermediate spaces. But this necessity rests on the fact that matter does not (as the merely mechanical investigators of nature assume) fill its space by absolute impenetrability, but by repulsive force; this force has its degree, which can be different in different matters. And since the degree of the repulsive force has of itself nothing in common with the attractive force, which is proportional to the quantity 534 of the matter, the repulsive force can with regard to one and the same attractive force be originally different in degree in different matters. And consequently the degree of the extension of the matters may as regards the same quantity of matter and, conversely, the quantity of matter may as regards the same volume, i.e., density of the matter, admit originally of very great specific differences. In this way one would not find it impossible to think of a matter (as one perhaps represents the ether) that entirely filled its space without any void and yet with incomparably less quantity of matter, at an equal volume, than any bodies we can subject to our experiments. The repulsive force in the ether must in relation to its proper attractive force be thought of as incomparably greater than in any other matter known to us. And the only reason why we merely assume such an ether, because it can be thought of, is as a foil to a hypothesis (that of empty spaces) which depends only on the assertion that such rarefied matter cannot be thought of without empty spaces. Besides the ether, no law whatever of attractive or of repulsive force may be risked on a priori conjectures; but everything, even universal attraction as the cause of gravity, must, together with the laws of such attraction, be concluded from data of experience. Still less will such conclusions in regard to chemical affinities be permitted to be tried otherwise than by means of experiment. For to comprehend original forces a priori according to their possibility lies generally beyond the horizon of our reason. Rather, all natural philosophy consists in the reduction of given forces apparently diverse to a smaller number of forces and powers sufficient for the explication of the actions of the former. But this reduction continues only to fundamental forces, beyond which our reason cannot go. And thus the investigation of metaphysics behind what lies at the basis of the empirical concept of matter is useful only for the purpose of leading natural philosophy as far as possible in the investigation of the dynamical grounds of explication, because these alone admit the hope of determinate laws, and consequently of a true rational coherence of explications.

This is all that metaphysics can ever accomplish for the construction of the concept of matter, and hence on behalf of the application of mathematics to natural science respecting the properties by which matter fills a space in determinate measure—namely, to regard these properties as dynamical and not as unconditioned original positions, such, for instance, as a merely mathematical treatment would postulate.

THIRD CHAPTER

Metaphysical Foundations of Mechanics

EXPLICATION 1

Matter is the movable insofar as it is something having a moving force.

Observation

Now, this is the third definition of matter. The merely dynamical concept could also regard matter as at rest. The moving force that was then taken into consideration concerned merely the filling of a certain space, without one's being permitted to regard the matter that filled the space as being itself moved. Repulsion was, therefore, an original moving force for imparting motion. On the other hand, in mechanics the force of a matter set in motion is regarded as present in order to impart this motion to another matter. But it is clear that the movable would have no moving force through its motion if it did not possess original moving forces, whereby it is active in every place where it exists before all proper motion. And it is clear that no uniform motion would be impressed on another matter by a matter whose motion lay in the path of the straight line in front of this other matter, unless both possessed original laws of repulsion; and that a matter could not by its motion compel another matter to follow it in the straight line (could not drag another after it), unless both possessed attractive forces. Hence all mechanical

537   laws presuppose dynamical ones; and a matter as moved can have no moving force except by means of its repulsion or attraction, upon which and with which it acts directly in its motion and thereby imparts its own motion to another matter. One will notice that I shall not make further mention here of the communication of motion by attraction (e.g., if perhaps a comet of stronger attractive power than the earth might in passing by the earth drag the earth after itself), but shall mention only the agency of repulsive forces, and hence such agency by pressure (as by means of tensed springs) or by impact. I shall do this because the application of the laws of repulsion in comparison with the case of attraction differs only with regard to the line of direction, but otherwise is the same in both cases.

EXPLICATION 2

The quantity of matter is the number of its movable [parts] in a determinate space. This quantity insofar as all its parts in their motion are regarded as simultaneously active (moving) is called the mass, and one says that a matter acts in mass when all its parts move in the same direction and at the same time exercise their moving force externally. A mass of determinate shape is called a body (in a mechanical sense). The quantity of motion (mechanically estimated) is what is estimated by means of the quantity of the moved matter and its velocity conjointly; phoronomically the quantity of motion consists merely in the degree of the moved matter's velocity.

PROPOSITION 1

The quantity of a matter can be estimated in comparison with every other matter only by its quantity of motion at a given velocity.

Proof

Matter is divisible to infinity; consequently, its quantity cannot be determined directly by means of the number of its parts. For if this occurs in the comparison of the given matter with a homogeneous one, in which case the quantity of the *538* matter is proportional to the magnitude of the volume, then this is contrary to the requirement of the proposition, namely, that the quantity of the matter is to be estimated in comparison with every other (even specifically different) matter. Therefore matter can neither directly nor indirectly be validly estimated in comparison with every other matter as long as one abstracts from its proper motion. Consequently, there remains no other universally valid measure of the matter than the quantity of its motion. But in this the difference of the motion, which rests on the different quantity of the matters, can only be given when the velocity is assumed to be equal among the compared matters, therefore, etc.

Note

The quantity of the motion of bodies is in compound proportion to the quantity of their matter and their velocity, i.e., it is all the same whether I make the quantity of the matter of a body doubly as great and retain the velocity, or whether I double the velocity and retain just this mass. For the determinate concept of a quantity is only possible through the construction of the quantum. But this construction as regards

the concept of quantity is nothing but the composition of the
equivalent; consequently, the construction of the quantity of
a motion is the composition of many motions equivalent
to one another. Now, it is all the same according to the
phoronomic propositions whether I impart to a movable
thing a certain degree of velocity, or to many equally movable
things all the smaller degrees of velocity that come from
the given velocity divided by the number of movable things.
Hereby arises at first an apparently phoronomic concept of
the quantity of a motion as composed of many motions external to one another but yet composed in a whole of united
movable points. If, now, these points are thought of as things
having moving force by means of their motion, then the mechanical concept of the quantity of the motion arises. But
in phoronomy it is not practicable to represent a motion as
composed of many motions existing externally to one another. This is because the movable (which in phoronomy is
represented as being without any moving force) in any com-
539   position with several of its own kind gives no distinction of
the quantity of the motion other than that quantity which
consists merely in the velocity. As the quantity of the motion
of one body is related to the quantity of the motion of another, so likewise is the quantity of its action related (by
"action" is to be understood its entire action). Those who assumed merely the magnitude of a space filled with resistance
(e.g., the height to which a body with a certain velocity can
rise against gravity, or the depth to which the same body can
penetrate into soft matters) as the measure of the entire action brought forward another law of moving forces as regards
actual motions, namely, that of the compound proportion
of the quantity of the matters and the squares of their velocities. But they overlooked the quantity of the action in the
given time in which the body traverses its space with less
velocity, and this quantity can alone be the measure of a
motion exhausted by a given uniform resistance. Hence there
can be no difference between living and dead forces if mov-

ing forces are regarded mechanically, i.e., as those which bodies have insofar as they are themselves moved, and the velocity of their motion may be finitely or infinitely small (mere endeavor toward motion). Rather, one might far more appropriately call those forces with which matter (even if one entirely abstracts from its proper motion or even its effort to move itself) acts on other matters dead forces, and hence call the original moving forces of dynamics dead forces. And one might, on the other hand, call all mechanical moving forces, i.e., by means of motion proper, living forces, if one does not pay any regard to the difference of the velocity, whose degree may be infinitely small. All of this holds providing these designations of dead and living forces deserve to be retained at all.

Observation

In order to avoid diffuseness, we are going to condense the elucidation of the preceding three statements into one observation.

That the quantity of matter can only be thought of as the number of its movable parts (external to one another), as the definition [Explication 2] expresses it, is a remarkable and fundamental statement of universal mechanics. For thereby is indicated that matter has no other quantity than that which consists in the multitude of its manifold parts external to one another. Consequently, matter has no degree of moving force with given velocity such that this degree might be independent of the aforementioned multitude and might be regarded merely as intensive quantity. Such would indeed be the case if matter consisted of monads, whose reality in every relation must have a degree that can be greater or smaller without being dependent upon a multitude of parts external to one another. As to what concerns the concept of mass in the same explication, it cannot, as is usually done, be taken to be the same as the concept of quantity. Fluid matters can

540

act by their own motion in mass, but they can also act in flow. In the so-called water-hammer, the water in striking acts in mass, i.e., with all its parts simultaneously; the same thing occurs in water that has been enclosed in a vessel and that presses by means of its weight upon the scales on which it stands. On the other hand, the water of a millstream does not act in mass on the paddle of the struck water wheel, i.e., with all its parts rushing simultaneously against the wheel, but the parts act only successively. Therefore if here the quantity of matter that is moved with a certain velocity and that has moving force is to be determined, then one must first of all look for the body of water, i.e., such quantity of matter as can produce the same action when it acts in mass with a certain velocity (with its weight). Hence one usually understands by the word "mass" the quantity of matter of a solid body (the vessel in which a fluid is enclosed takes the place of its solidity). Finally, in regard to the proposition [Proposition 1] together with its appended note, there is something strange involved in the fact that according to the propostion, the quantity of the matter must be estimated by the quantity of the motion with given velocity, while according to the note, on the other hand, the quantity of the motion (of a body, because that of a point consists merely in the degree of its velocity) at the same velocity must be estimated by means of the quantity of the moved matter. All of this seems to revolve in a circle and to promise no determinate concept either of the one or of the other. This supposed circle would be actual if it were a reciprocal derivation of two identical concepts from one another. But it contains, on the one hand, only the explication of a concept and, on the other, the explication of the application of the concept to experience. The quantity of the movable in space is the quantity of the matter, but this quantity of the matter (the multitude of the movable) manifests itself in experience only by the quantity of the motion at equal velocity (e.g., by equilibrium).

There is yet to be noted that the quantity of matter is the

quantity of substance in the movable and, consequently, is not the magnitude of a certain quality of matter (of repulsion or attraction, which are cited in dynamics), and that the quantum of substance here signifies nothing but the mere number of the movable parts, which constitutes matter. For only this number of the moved parts can with the same velocity give a difference in the quantity of the motion. But the fact that   *541* the moving force which a matter possesses in its proper motion alone manifests its quantity of substance rests on the concept of substance as the ultimate subject (which is not a further predicate of another subject) in space; for this reason this subject can have no other quantity than that of the multitude of its homogeneous parts, being external to one another. Now, the proper motion of matter is a predicate which determines such motion's subject (the movable) and with regard to matter as a multitude of movable parts indicates the plurality of the moved subjects (at equal velocity in the same direction); this is not the case with dynamical properties, whose quantity can also be the quantity of the action of a single subject (e.g., a particle of air can have more or less elasticity). Because of all of this it is clear that the quantity of substance in a matter must be estimated mechanically, i.e., by the quantity of the proper motion of the matter, and not dynamically, by the quantity of its original moving forces. Nevertheless, original attraction as the cause of universal gravitation can indeed provide a measure of the quantity of matter and its substance (as actually happens in the comparison of matters by weighing), although there seems to be laid at the foundation here not the proper motion of the attracting matter but a dynamical measure, namely, attractive force. But in the case of this force, the action of one matter occurs with all its parts directly on all parts of another matter; and hence the action is (at equal distances) obviously proportional to the number of the parts. Because of this fact the attracting body itself thereby also imparts the velocity of its proper motion (by means of the resistance of the attracted

Observation

Substance is possible only in space and according to the conditions of space, and hence is possible only as object of the external senses. The essential thing which characterizes substance in this proof is that its quantity cannot be increased or diminished unless substance arises or perishes. Therefore, inasmuch as any quantity of an object that is possible only in space must consist of parts external to one another, these, if they are real (something movable), must necessarily be substances. On the other hand, that which is regarded as object of the internal sense can as substance have a quantity that does not consist of parts external to one another and whose parts are therefore not substances. The arising or perishing of this quantity, consequently, must not be the arising or perishing of substance; and the increase or diminution of such quantity is therefore possible without detriment to the principle of the permanence of substance. To wit, consciousness has a degree that may be greater or smaller without any substance needing to arise or perish. And hence the clarity of the representations of my soul has such a degree, and in consequence of this fact the faculty of consciousness, namely, apperception—and along with this faculty even the substance of the soul—has also such a degree. But inasmuch as a total disappearance of this faculty of apperception must finally ensue upon the gradual diminution of the same, even the substance of the soul would be subjected to a gradual perishing, even though the soul were of a simple nature, because this disappearance of its fundamental force could not ensue through division (separation of substance from a composite) but, as it were, by expiration, and even this not in a moment, but by the gradual remission of its degree, from whatever cause. The "I", the universal correlate of apperception and itself merely a thought, designates as a mere prefix a thing of indeterminate signification,

namely, the subject of all predicates without any condition
to distinguish this representation of the subject from that of
543 a something in general, namely, substance; by the expression
"substance", one has no concept as to what this substance
is. On the other hand, the concept of a matter as substance
is the concept of the movable in space. Hence it is no won-
der if permanence of substance can be proved of matter
but not of the soul. This is because in the case of matter there
follows from its concept, namely, that it is the movable,
which is only possible in space, the fact that what has quantity in matter contains a plurality of real parts external to
one another, and hence contains a plurality of substances.
Consequently, the quantity of matter can be diminished only
by division, which is no disappearance; such disappearance
would, according to the law of permanence, be impossible
in the case of matter. The thought "I" is, on the other hand,
no concept at all but only an internal perception. Therefore,
from this thought, nothing at all can be concluded (except the
complete distinction of an object of the internal sense from
what is thought merely as object of the external senses);
consequently, the permanence of the soul as substance cannot be concluded from the thought "I".

PROPOSITION 3

Second law of mechanics: Every change of matter has an
external cause. (Every body remains in its state of rest or
motion in the same direction and with the same velocity
unless it is compelled by an external cause to forsake this
state.[45])

Proof

(In universal metaphysics there is laid down the proposition

[45] [This is Newton's first law of motion.]

that every change has a cause;[46] here [in mechanics] there is only to be proved of matter that its change must always have an external cause.) Matter as mere object of the external senses has no other determinations than those of external relations in space and hence undergoes no changes except by motion. With regard to such change, insofar as it is an exchange of one motion with another, or of motion with rest, and vice versa, a cause of such change must be found (according to the principle of metaphysics). But this cause cannot be internal, for matter has no absolutely internal determinations and grounds of determination. Hence all change of a matter is based upon an external cause (i.e., a body remains etc.).

Observation   544

This mechanical law alone must be called the law of inertia (*lex inertiae*); the law that every action has an equal and opposite reaction cannot bear this name. For the latter says what matter does, but the former only what it does not do, and this is better adapted to the expression of inertia. The inertia of matter is and signifies nothing but its lifelessness, as matter in itself. Life means the capacity of a substance to determine itself to act from an internal principle, of a finite substance to determine itself to change, and of a material substance to determine itself to motion or rest as change of its state. Now, we know of no other internal principle of a substance to change its state but desire and no other internal activity whatever but thought, along with what depends upon such desire, namely, feeling of pleasure or displeasure, and appetite or will. But these determining grounds and actions do not at all belong to the representations of the external senses and hence also not to the determinations of matter as matter. Therefore, all matter as such is lifeless. The prop-

---

[46] [Cf. *Critique of Pure Reason*, B 232–256.]

osition of inertia says so much and no more. If we seek the
cause of any change whatever of matter in life, we shall have
to seek this cause at once in another substance different from
matter, although bound up with it. For in natural knowledge
it is necessary to know first the laws of matter as such and to
clear them of the admixture of all other active causes before
one connects these laws with such causes, in order to distinguish how and what each such law brings about of itself
alone. The possibility of a natural science proper rests entirely upon the law of inertia (along with the law of the
permanence of substance). The opposite of this, and therefore the death of all natural philosophy, would be hylozoism.
From the very concept of inertia as mere lifelessness there
follows of itself the fact that inertia does not signify a positive
effort of something to maintain its state. Only living things
are called inert in this latter sense, inasmuch as they have a
representation of another state which they abhor and strive
against with all their power.

PROPOSITION 4

Third mechanical law: In all communication of motion,
action and reaction are always equal to one another.[47]

Proof

(The proposition that all external action in the world is
reciprocal action must be borrowed from universal meta-
545   physics.[48] Hence in order to stay within the bounds of mechanics, one only has to show that this reciprocal action—
actio muta—is at the same time reaction—*reactio*. But the

---

[47] [This is Newton's third law of motion.]
[48] [Cf. *Critique of Pure Reason*, B 256–262.]

aforementioned metaphysical law of community cannot here be entirely left out without disrupting the completeness of the insight.) All active relations of matters in space and all •changes of these relations insofar as they can be causes of certain actions must always be represented as reciprocal. That is, since all change of such relations is motion, no motion of a body with reference to one absolutely at rest which is thereby also to be set in motion can be thought of. Rather, this latter body must be represented only as relatively at rest with regard to the space to which it is referred; this body must be represented as moved, together with this space but in the opposite direction,[49] with the very same quantity of motion in absolute space as the moved body has in absolute space toward this one that is relatively at rest. For the change of relation (and hence the motion) is completely reciprocal between both bodies; by as much as the one body approaches every part of the other, by so much this other approaches every part of the first. And since the main thing here is not the empirical space surrounding both bodies but only the line lying between them (inasmuch as these bodies are considered merely in relation to one another according to the influence which the motion of the one can have on the change of state of the other, abstraction being made of all relation to empirical space), their motion is regarded as determinable only in absolute space, in which each of the two bodies must equally participate in the motion attributed to the one in relative space, since there is no ground for attributing more motion to one of them than to the other. On this footing, the motion of a body A toward another one B at rest, with regard to which the former can thereby be moving, is reduced to absolute space, i.e., the motion in question is considered to be a relation of efficient

[49] [That is, in the direction opposite to that of the motion of the first body toward the second body. This whole sentence becomes clearer when one refers to the discussion below, especially the construction of the communication of motion.]

causes referred merely to one another; and so the motion is considered as if both bodies equally participate in this motion, which in the appearance[50] is attributed only to the body A. This can occur only in the following way. The veloc-ity which in the relative space is attributed only to the body A is divided between A and B in inverse proportion to their masses; A is given only its velocity in absolute space, while, on the other hand, B, together with the relative space in which it rests, is given its velocity in the opposite direction. 546 In this way the same appearance [*Erscheinung*] of the motion is perfectly retained. The action in the community of both bodies is constructed as follows. Let a body A be in

FIGURE 5

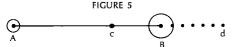

motion toward the body B with a velocity $=$ AB with regard to the relative space; the body B is at rest with regard to the same space. Let the velocity AB be divided into two parts, Ac and Bc, which are related to one another inversely as the masses B and A. Represent A as moved with the velocity Ac in absolute space, but B with the velocity Bc in the opposite direction together with the relative space. Thus both motions are opposite and equal to one another; and since they mutually destroy one another, both bodies put themselves relatively to one another, i.e., in absolute space, in a state of rest. But, now, B together with the relative space was in motion with the velocity Bc in the direction BA; this velocity is exactly opposed to that of the body A, namely, AB. Hence if the motion of the body B is destroyed by impact, then the motion of the relative space is not therefore destroyed. Hence after the impact, the relative space with regard to both bodies A and B (which now rest in absolute space) moves in the direction BA with the velocity Bc, or, what is the same thing, both

---

[50] [*Erscheinung*, which can also be rendered as "phenomenon."]

bodies after the impact move with equal velocity Bd = Bc in the direction of the impacting AB. According to the foregoing, however, the quantity of motion of the body B in the direction and with the velocity Bc, and hence likewise the quantity of motion of B in the direction Bd with the same velocity, is equal to the quantity of motion of the body A with the velocity and in the direction Ac. Consequently, the effect, i.e., the motion Bd, which the body B receives by impact in relative space, and hence also the action of the body A with the velocity Ac, is always equal to the reaction Bc. The very same law (as mathematical mechanics teaches) suffers no alteration when, instead of the impact upon a resting body, an impact of the body upon a moved one is assumed; similarly, the communication of motion by impact is distinguished from that by traction only in the direction in which the matters oppose one another in their motions. Because of all this there follows that in all communication of motion, action and reaction are always equal to one another (that every impact can communicate the motion of one body to another only by means of an equal counterimpact, every pressure by means of an equal counterpressure, and, similarly, every traction only by an equal countertraction).[51]

547

[51] Inasmuch as the motion of a body was considered in phoronomy merely with regard to its space as change of relation in space, it was all the same whether I wanted to ascribe the motion to the body in space, or instead ascribe to the relative space an equal but opposite motion;* both gave fully the same appearance [Erscheinung]. The quantity of motion of the space was merely its velocity, and hence the quantity of motion of the body was likewise nothing but its velocity (for which reason the body could be regarded as a mere movable point). But in mechanics, a body is regarded as in motion toward another, respecting which it has a causal relation through its motion, namely, the relation that in the former's moving itself either by its approach through the force of impenetrability or by its withdrawal through the force of attraction, it comes into community with this other body. Because of this fact, whether I want to ascribe an opposite motion to one of these bodies, or to the space, is no longer all the same. For now another concept of the quantity of motion comes into play, namely, not that which is thought merely

* [See above, Ak. 487–488.]

548   Note 1

From the foregoing there follows the natural law, which is not unimportant for universal mechanics, that every body, however great its mass may be, must be movable by the impact of every other, however small its mass or velocity may be. For to the motion of A in the direction AB there necessarily corresponds an equal opposite motion of B in the direction BA. Both motions destroy one another in absolute space by impact. But thereby both bodies receive a velocity Bd $=$ Bc in the direction of the impacting one; consequently, the body B is movable by every force of impact, however small.

Note 2

This is, then, the mechanical law of the equality of action and reaction. This law is based on the fact that no communication of motion takes place except insofar as a community

547   with regard to the space and consists only in the velocity, but that whereby at the same time the quantity of the substance (as moving cause) must be taken into consideration. And it is here no longer optional but necessary to assume both bodies as moved, and indeed moved with an equal quantity of motion in an opposite direction. But when the one body is relatively at rest with regard to its space, then it is necessary to attribute the requisite motion to this body together with its space. For the one cannot act on the other by this [first] one's own motion except by approach through repulsive force or by withdrawal through attractive force. Since, now, both forces always act equally and reciprocally in opposite directions, no body can act upon another body by means of these forces through its motion except just so much as the other body reacts with an equal quantity of motion. Hence no body can impart motion through its motion to an absolutely resting body, but this second body must be moved (together with its space) in the opposite direction with just that quantity of motion which is the same as that which it is to receive through the motion of the first body and in the direction of this first one. The reader will easily see that in spite of the somewhat unusual character which this mode of representation of the communication of motion has in itself, this representation can nevertheless be placed in the clearest light, if one does not shrink from the diffuseness of the explanation.

of these motions is presupposed. And so this law is based on the fact that no body hits another that is at rest with regard to this first body, but, rather, the first body hits the second body insofar as the second is at rest with regard to its space; and so the first hits the second only insofar as the second together with its space moves in equal measure in the opposite direction with the motion which then falls to the first body as its relative share and which as a whole first of all gives the quantity of motion that we would attribute to this first body in absolute space.[52] For no motion [of a body] that is to be moving with regard to another body can be absolute; but if the motion is relative with regard to this other body, then there is no relation in space that is not reciprocal and equal. But there is yet another, namely, a dynamical, law of the equality of the action and reaction of matters, not insofar as one matter communicates its motion to another, but insofar as this first matter originally imparts its motion to the second one and by means of the second one's resistance the motion is at the same time produced in the first. This can be easily demonstrated in a similar way. For if the matter A attracts the matter B, then A compels B to approach A, or, what is the same thing, A resists the force with which B endeavors to withdraw. But inasmuch as it is all the same whether B withdraws from A or A from B, this resistance is at the same time a resistance which the body B exercises against A insofar as A endeavors to withdraw from B, and hence traction and countertraction are equal to one another.   *549* In the same way, if A repels the matter B, then A resists the approach of B. But since it is all the same whether B approaches A or A approaches B, so B also resists just as much the approach of A; hence pressure and counterpressure are also always equal to one another.

[52] [This is an extremely difficult sentence to translate. Its meaning becomes clear when one refers to Kant's construction of the communication of motion above.]

Observation 1

This is, then, the construction of the communication of motion. This construction at the same time carries with it as its necessary condition the law of the equality of action and reaction. Newton did not at all trust himself to prove this law a priori, but appealed to experience to prove it. Other people for the sake of this law introduced into natural science a special force of matter under the name of the force of inertia (vis inertiae), first mentioned by Kepler, and thus they also really derived it from experience. Finally, still others posited the concept of a mere communication of motion which they regarded as a gradual transference of the motion of one body into another, whereby the moving body must lose exactly as much motion as it imparts to the moved one until it impresses no more motion on the latter (when, namely, it has arrived at an equality of velocity with the latter and its velocity is in the same direction as that of the latter).[53]

[53] The equality of the action with the—in this case falsely called—reaction turns out just as well when a person under the hypothesis of the transfusion of motions from one body into another allows the moved body A to give up its entire motion in one moment to the resting body. Consequently, the body A would rest after the impact; this situation would be inevitable as soon as both bodies were thought of as absolutely hard (a property that must be distinguished from elasticity). But inasmuch as this law of motion would in its application accord neither with experience nor with itself, one would know of nothing else to do but deny the existence of absolutely hard bodies. This would be tantamount to admitting the contingency of this law, inasmuch as it is to depend on the special quality of the matters which move one another. In our presentation of this law, on the other hand, it is quite the same whether one wants to think of the bodies that hit one another as absolutely hard or not. But it is quite inconceivable to me how the transfusionists of motion intend to explain in their way the motion of elastic bodies by impact. For it is clear that the resting body does not insofar as it is merely resting receive motion which the hitting body loses, but that the resting body in impact exercises actual force in the opposite direction against the hitting body, as though to compress a spring lying between them. To this end there is required on the part of the resting body just as much actual motion (but in the opposite direction) as the moving body on its part needs for this end.

In this way they actually destroyed all reaction, i.e., all really reacting force of the one hit against the one hitting (which might perhaps be capable of tensing a spring). Moreover, *550* they do not prove what is actually meant in this aforementioned law, i.e., they did not at all explicate the communication of motion according to the possibility of such communication. For the words "transference of motion from one body to another" explicate nothing. And if one might not want to take this transference literally (since it is opposed to the principle, *accidentia non migrant e substantiis in substantias*[54]), as though motion were poured from one body into another, like water from one glass into another; then the problem here is how to make conceivable this possibility whose explication rests exactly on the same ground from which the law of the equality of action and reaction is derived. One cannot at all think how the motion of a body A must necessarily be connected with the motion of another one B except by one's thinking that there are forces belonging to both (dynamically) before all motion, e.g., repulsion. And now with these forces one can prove that the motion of the body A by approach toward B is necessarily connected with the approach of B toward A and, if B is regarded as at rest, is connected with the motion of B together with its space toward A, insofar as the bodies with their (original) moving forces are considered as in motion merely relatively to one another. This latter can thereby be fully comprehended a priori, viz., that whether the body B with respect to its empirically cognizable space be at rest or moved, it must be regarded as necessarily moved with respect to the body A and indeed as moved in an opposite direction. If this were not so, no influence of A upon the repulsive force of both bodies would occur; and without such an influence, no mechanical action whatever of matters on one another, i.e., no communication of motion by impact, is possible.

[54] ["Accidents do not wander from substances to substances."]

Observation 2

The designation force of inertia (*vis inertiae*) must, then, in spite of the famous name of its originator, be entirely dismissed from natural science. This must be done not only because this designation carries with it a contradiction in the expression itself, or because the law of inertia (lifelessness) might thereby be easily confused with the law of reaction in every communicated motion, but mainly because through this confusion the erroneous representation of those who are not correctly acquainted with the mechanical laws would be maintained and strengthened. According to this erroneous representation, the reaction of bodies, of which we are speaking under the name of the force of inertia, would result in the fact that the motion in the world would be consumed, diminished, or destroyed. However, the mere communication of motion would not by such reaction be brought about, inasmuch as the moving body would have to expend a part of its motion merely to overcome the inertia of the resting one (such expense being pure loss), and with the remaining part alone could it set the latter in motion; but if no motion remained, then it would not by its impact bring the latter into motion because of the latter's great mass. Nothing but the opposite motion of another body can resist a motion, but this other's rest can in no way resist a motion. Here, then, inertia of matter, i.e., mere incapacity to move of itself, is not the cause of a resistance. A special and entirely peculiar force merely to resist, but without being able to move a body, would under the name of a force of inertia be a word without any meaning. The three laws of universal mechanics might, then, be more appropriately designated the law of the subsistence, the inertia, and the reaction of matters (*lex Subsistentiae, Inertiae et Antagonismi*), as regards all the changes of matters. That these laws, and hence all the propositions of the present science,

551

exactly answer to the categories of substance, causality, and community,[55] insofar as these concepts are applied to matter, requires no further discussion.

GENERAL
OBSERVATION
ON MECHANICS

The communication of motion takes place only by means of such moving forces as also inhere in a matter at rest (impenetrability and attraction). The action of a moving force on a body in one moment is the solicitation of the body. The velocity of the body brought about by its solicitation, insofar as this velocity can increase in equal proportion to the time, is the moment of acceleration. (The moment of acceleration must therefore contain only an infinitely small velocity, because otherwise the body would attain through the moment of acceleration an infinite velocity in a given time; but this is impossible. Moreover, the possibility of acceleration in general through a continuous moment of acceleration rests on the law of inertia.) The solicitation of matter by expansive force (e.g., of compressed air that bears a weight) occurs always with a finite velocity. But the velocity which is thereby impressed upon (or taken away from) another body can only be infinitely small; for expansive force is only a superficial force, or, what is the same thing, is the motion of an infinitely small quantum of matter, and such motion must, consequently, occur with finite velocity in order to be equal to the motion of a body of finite mass with infinitely small velocity (weight). On the other hand, attraction is a penetrating force by means of which a finite quan-

[55] [Cf. *Critique of Pure Reason*, B 106.]

tum of matter exercises moving force on a similarly finite
quantum of another matter. The solicitation of attraction
552   must, then, be infinitely small because it is equal to the moment of acceleration (which must always be infinitely small);
this is not the case as regards repulsion, where an infinitely
small part of matter is to impress a moment on a finite part.
No attraction with a finite velocity can be thought of without the matter's having to penetrate itself by its own attractive force. For the attraction which a finite quantity of matter
exercises on another finite quantity with a finite velocity must
in all points of the compression be superior to every finite
velocity with which the matter reacts by means of its impenetrability but only with an infinitely small part of the
quantity of its matter. If attraction is only a superficial force,
as one thinks of cohesion, then the opposite of this would
result. But it is impossible to think of cohesion in such a way,
if it is to be true attraction (and not merely external compression).

An absolutely hard body would be one whose parts attracted one another so strongly that they could not be separated by any weight nor be altered in their position with
regard to one another. Now, the parts of the matter of such
a body would have to attract one another with a moment of
acceleration that would be infinite as compared with the
moment of acceleration of gravity, but would be finite as
compared with the moment of acceleration of the mass that
is thereby put into motion. Because of this, resistance by
impenetrability as expansive force, since resistance always
occurs with an infinitely small quantity of matter, would have
to occur with more than finite velocity of solicitation, i.e.,
the matter would endeavor to extend itself with infinite
velocity; but this is impossible. Therefore, an absolutely hard
body, i.e., one that would oppose a body moved with finite
velocity and would do so in one moment with a resistance
on impact equal to the whole force of this latter body, is
impossible. Consequently, a matter produces by its impene-

trability or cohesion only an infinitely small resistance in one moment to the force of a body in finite motion. From this there follows, now, the mechanical law of continuity (*lex continui mechanica*), namely, in no body is the state of rest or motion—and in the latter, of velocity or direction—changed by impact in one moment, but only in a certain time through an infinite series of intermediate states whose difference from one another is smaller than that between the first and last such states. A moved body that hits a matter is thus not brought to rest by the latter's resistance all at once but only by a continuous retardation, or a body that was at rest is set into motion only by a continuous acceleration, or a body is changed from one degree of velocity to another only according to the same rule. Similarly, the direction of a body's motion that is changed into such a direction as forms an angle with the former one does so only by means of all possible intermediate directions, i.e., by means of motion in a curved line (this law, for a similar reason, can also be extended to the change of state of a body by means of attraction). This *lex continui* is based on the law of the inertia of matter. On the other hand, the metaphysical[56] law of continuity must be extended to all change (internal as well as external) in general and hence would be based on the mere concept of a change in general, as quantity, and on the concept of the generation of such change (such generation necessarily proceeds continuously in a certain time, like time itself). And so this metaphysical law has no place here.

553

---

56 [Kant might more appropriately have said "transcendental" here.]

FOURTH
CHAPTER

Metaphysical Foundations of Phenomenology[57]

EXPLICATION

Matter is the movable insofar as it can as such be an object of experience.

Observation

Motion, like everything that is represented through sense, is given only as appearance.[58] In order that the representation of motion may become experience, there is required in addition that something be thought through the understanding, namely, in addition to the way in which this representation of motion inheres in the subject, there is required further the determination of an object by means of this representation.

---

[57] [By "phenomenology" Kant means the doctrine of appearance (*Erscheinungslehre*). See Kant's footnote (71) below, Ak. 559–560.]

[58] [Cf. *Critique of Pure Reason,* trans. Norman Kemp Smith (London: Macmillan and Co., 1929, and St. Martin's Press: New York, 1964), B 34, p. 65: "The undetermined object of an empirical intuition is entitled *appearance.*" This and the following quotations from the *Critique* are printed by permission of St. Martin's Press. Page numbers refer to their paperback edition.]

Therefore, the movable as such becomes an object of experience when a certain object (here, a material thing) is thought
as determined with regard to the predicate of motion. But
motion is change of relation in space. There are, then, always
two correlates[59] here. Firstly,[60] in the appearance, change
can be attributed to one just as well as to the other of these
correlates, and either the one or the other can be called
moved inasmuch as both attributions are equivalent. Or,
secondly,[61] one of these correlates must in the experience
be thought as moved to the exclusion of the other. Or,
thirdly,[62] both of these correlates must necessarily through
reason be represented as moved at the same time. In the
appearance, which contains nothing but the relation in the
motion (according to the change of the relation), none of   *555*
these determinations are contained. But when the movable
as such, namely, according to its motion, is to be thought as
determined, i.e., for the sake of a possible experience, then
it is necessary to indicate the conditions under which the
object (matter) must be determined in one way or another
by the predicate of motion. Here the question is not of the
transformation of illusion [*Schein*] into truth, but of appearance [*Erscheinung*] into experience. For as regards illusion,
the understanding is always involved with its judgments determining[63] an object, although it is always in danger of
taking the subjective for the objective; but in the appearance, no judgment at all of the understanding is to be

[59] [The two correlates of motion are matter and space.]

[60] [Cf. Proposition 1 below.]

[61] [Cf. Proposition 2 below.]

[62] [Cf. Proposition 3 below.]

[63] [Cf. *Critique of Pure Reason*, B 93, p. 105: "Judgment is therefore the
mediate knowledge of an object, that is, the representation of a representation
of it. In every judgment there is a concept which holds of many representations, and among them of a given representation that is immediately related
to an object."]

found.[64] It is necessary to note this not only here but in the whole of philosophy, because otherwise there is always misunderstanding when the question is about appearances and this expression is taken as identical in meaning with that of illusion.

PROPOSITION 1

The rectilinear motion of a matter with regard to an empirical space, as distinguished from the opposite motion of this space, is a merely possible predicate. The rectilinear motion of a matter in no relation to a matter outside of itself, i.e., such rectilinear motion thought of as absolute, is impossible.

Proof

In the case of a body moved in relative space, whether this space is said to be at rest, or, conversely, this space is said to be moved with equal velocity in the opposite direction and the body to be at rest—in this case, I say, there is no disagreement as to what belongs to the object, but only as to what belongs to the relation of the object to the subject; and hence there is no disagreement concerning what belongs to the experience, but only to the appearance. For if the spectator puts himself in the same space that is at rest, then he says that the body is moved; if he puts himself (at least in thought) in another space enclosing the aforementioned one and the body is at rest with regard to this enclosing space, then the aforementioned relative space is said to be moved. Therefore, in experience (in a cognition that validly determines the object for all appearances), there is no difference what-

[64] [Cf. *ibid.,* B 350, p. 297: "It is therefore correct to say that the senses do not err—not because they always judge rightly but because they do not judge at all. Truth and error, therefore, and consequently also illusion as leading to error, are only to be found in the judgment, i.e., only in the relation of the object to our understanding."]

ever between the motion of the body in relative space and the resting of the body in absolute space with the equal but opposite motion of the relative space. Now, the repre-   *556* sentation of an object by one of two predicates that are equivalent regarding the object and different from one another only regarding the subject and his mode of representation is not a determination according to a disjunctive judgment, but is merely a choice according to an alternative one. (The disjunctive judgment assumes for the determination of the object one of two objectively opposed predicates to the exclusion of its contrary. But the alternative judgment assumes for the determination of the object one of two judgments that are indeed objectively equivalent, but are subjectively opposed to one another without the contrary's being excluded from the object—and hence assumes this one judgment by mere choice.[65]) This means that through the concept of motion as object of experience, there is no determination (and hence an equivalence) whether a body is represented as moved in relative space, or the relative space is represented as moved with regard to the body. Now, that which is in itself undetermined as regards two mutually opposed predicates is thus far merely possible. Therefore, the rectilinear motion of a matter in empirical space, in contradistinction to the equal and opposite motion of the space, is in experience a merely possible predicate. This was the first point in the proposition.

Further, a relation, and hence also a change of this relation, i.e., motion, can be an object of experience only insofar as both of motion's correlates[66] are objects of experience; but pure space, which is also called absolute space in contradistinction to relative (empirical) space, is no object of experience and is nothing at all. Because of this, rectilinear

---

[65] Concerning this distinction of disjunctive and alternative opposition, more in the general observation to this chapter. [Cf. Kant's footnote (71) below, Ak. 559–560.]

[66] [That is, matter and space.]

motion without reference to anything empirical, i.e., absolute motion, is utterly impossible. This was the second point in the proposition.

Observation

This proposition determines the modality of motion with regard to phoronomy.

PROPOSITION 2

557

The circular motion of a matter, in contradistinction to the opposite motion of the space, is an actual predicate of matter. On the other hand, the opposite motion of a relative space, taken instead of the motion of the body, is no actual motion of the body; if this opposite motion of a relative space is held to be an actual motion of the body, then such motion is a mere illusion [Schein].

Proof

Circular motion is (like every curvilinear motion) a continuous change of rectilinear motion; and since this change is itself a continuous change of relation with regard to external space, circular motion is a change of the change of these external relations in space and, consequently, is a continuous arising of new motions. Now, according to the law of inertia, a motion insofar as it arises must have an external cause. But the body at every point of this circle is (according to the very same law) endeavoring to proceed in the straight line touching the circle, and this motion acts against the aforementioned external cause. Hence every body in circular motion manifests by its motion a moving force. Now, the motion of the space, in contradistinction to the motion of the body, is merely phoronomic and has no moving force. Consequently, the judgment that here either the body is moved or else the space is moved in the opposite direction is a disjunctive one, by which, if the one member, namely, the motion of the body, is posited, then the other member, namely, the motion of the space, is excluded. Therefore, the circular motion of a body, in contradistinction to the motion of the space, is an actual motion. Even though according to the appearance [*Erscheinung*] the motion of the space agrees with the circular motion of the body, nevertheless in the complex of all appearances, i.e., of possible experience, the former motion conflicts with the latter; and hence the former is nothing but mere illusion [*Schein*].

Observation

This proposition determines the modality of motion with regard to dynamics. For a motion which cannot take place without the influence of a continuously acting external moving force proves directly or indirectly original moving forces of matter, either of repulsion or of attraction. By the way, on the present subject, one can refer to the latter part of Newton's scholium to the definitions with which he begins his *Mathematical Principles of Natural Philosophy*. From this it will become clear that the circular motion of two bodies around a common center (and hence also the rotation of   *558* the earth on its axis) even in empty space, and hence without any possible comparison through experience with external space, can nevertheless be cognized by means of experience, and that therefore a motion, which is a change of external relations in space, can be empirically given, although this space itself is not empirically given and is no object of experience. This paradox deserves to be solved.

PROPOSITION 3

In every motion of a body whereby it is moving with regard to another body, an opposite and equal motion of this other body is necessary.

Proof

According to the third law of mechanics (Proposition 4), the communication of the motion of the bodies is possible only through the community of their originally moving forces, and this community is possible only through reciprocal opposite and equal motion. The motion of both bodies is therefore actual. However, the actuality of this motion does not rest (as in the second proposition[67]) on the influence of external forces, but follows immediately and inevitably from the concept of the relation of the moved in space to every other thing thereby movable; therefore, the motion of this latter is necessary.

Observation

This proposition determines the modality of motion with regard to mechanics. That these three propositions, moreover, determine the motion of matter with regard to its possibility, actuality, and necessity, and hence with regard to all three categories of modality,[68] is obvious of itself.

[67] [Of phenomenology.]

[68] [Cf. *Critique of Pure Reason,* B 106.]

GENERAL
OBSERVATION
ON PHENOMENOLOGY

Hence there are manifested here three concepts whose employment in universal natural science is unavoidable, and whose exact determination is for this reason necessary, although this determination is not so easy and comprehensible. They are, namely, the concept of motion in relative (movable) space; secondly, the concept of motion in absolute (immovable) space; thirdly, the concept of relative motion in general, in contradistinction to absolute motion. The concept of absolute space is laid at the foundation of all of them. But how do we come by this unusual concept, and upon what does the necessity of its employment rest?   *559*

It cannot be an object of experience, for space without matter is no object of perception; and yet it is a necessary concept of reason, and is therefore nothing but a mere idea.[69] For in order that motion may be given even as appearance, there is required an empirical representation of space with regard to which the movable is to change its relation; but the space which is to be perceived must be material and hence, according to the concept of matter in general, must itself be movable. Now, in order to think of this space as moved, one can think of it only as contained in a space of greater compass and can assume this latter to be at rest. But this latter space admits of being arranged in just the same way as regards a still more enlarged space, and so on to infinity without ever by experience arriving at an immovable (immaterial) space with regard to which motion or rest could

[69] [See *ibid.*, B 366–377.]

be attributed absolutely to any matter. Rather, the concept of these relational determinations will have to be constantly changed according as the movable is considered to be related to one or the other of these spaces. Now, the condition for regarding something as at rest or moved is always again and again conditioned to infinity in relative space; from this fact the following things become clear. Firstly, all motion or rest can be merely relative and neither can be absolute, i.e., matter can be thought of as moved or at rest only in relation to matter and never as regards mere space without matter. Therefore, absolute motion, i.e., such as is thought of without any reference of one matter to another, is simply impossible. Secondly, for this very reason no concept of motion or rest in relative space and valid for every appearance is possible. But a space must be thought of in which this relative space can be thought of as moved; the determination of such a space does not further depend on any other empirical space and hence is not again conditioned—that is, an absolute space, to which all relative motions can be referred, must be thought of.[70] In such a space everything empirical is movable. Consequently, in it all motions of material things can be valid as merely relative to one another, and as alternatively-reciprocal;[71] but none can be valid as absolute

---

[70] [See *ibid.*, B 377–389.]

[71] In logic the "either-or" always denotes a disjunctive judgment; for if one member is true, the other must be false. For instance, a body is either moved or not moved, i.e., at rest; for one speaks there simply of the relation of the cognition to the object. It is different in the doctrine of appearance [*Erscheinungslehre*], where there is involved the relation to the subject in order to determine according to this relation the relation of the objects. For here the proposition that the body is either moved and the space at rest or vice versa is not a disjunctive proposition with an objective reference but only a subjective one, and both of the judgments contained in this proposition are alternatively valid. In this very same phenomenology, when motion is considered not merely phoronomically but, rather, dynamically, the disjunctive proposition is, on the other hand, to be taken with an objective meaning, i.e., instead of the rotation of a body I cannot assume the rest of the body and, on the other hand, the opposite motion of the space. But even

motion or rest (since, inasmuch as one is called moved, the   *560*
other, with reference to which this former is moved, is nevertheless represented as absolutely at rest). Absolute space is,
then, necessary not as a concept of an actual object but as
an idea that is to serve as a rule for considering all motion
therein only as relative.[72] All motion and rest must be reduced to absolute space if the appearance of these is to be
transformed into a determinate concept of experience (all
appearances being united by this concept).

   Thus the rectilinear motion of a body in relative space is
reduced to absolute space when I think of the body as in
itself at rest but think of the relative space as moved in the
opposite direction in absolute space (which does not fall under the senses). Representing such rectilinear motion in this
way gives exactly the same appearance.[73] By means of this
representation all possible appearances of rectilinear motions which a body might simultaneously have are reduced
to that concept of experience which unites them all together,
namely, the concept of merely relative motion and rest.

   Inasmuch as circular motion can, according to the second
proposition, be given as actual motion in experience even
without reference to an external, empirically given space, it
does indeed seem to be absolute motion. For relative motion
with regard to an external space (e.g., the rotation of the
earth on its axis relative to the stars of the heavens) is an
appearance in whose stead the opposite motion of this space

---

when motion is considered mechanically (as when a body rushes toward another that is apparently at rest), even then the disjunctive form of the judgment as regards the object is to be used distributively; and so the motion must
not be attributed either to the one body or to the other, but an equal share
must be attributed to each. This distinction of alternative, disjunctive, and
distributive determination of a concept as regards contrary predicates has its
importance, but cannot be further discussed here.   .

[72] [See *Critique of Pure Reason,* B 670–696.]

[73] [Gives the same appearance as thinking of the body as moved in a space
that is at rest.]

/

(of the heavens) in the same time can be posited as fully equivalent to the former motion. But according to this second proposition, in experience the latter motion must never
561   be posited instead of the former, and hence the aforementioned rotation is not to be represented as externally relative, and thus it sounds as though this kind of motion is assumed to be absolute.

But it is well to note that here the question is about the true (actual) motion, which does not seem to be such. And hence if one might want to judge of this motion merely according to empirical relations to space, then it could be regarded as rest. In other words, the question is about the true motion, in contradistinction to illusion, but is not about the motion as absolute, in contrast to relative. And hence even though circular motion exhibits in its appearance no change of place, i.e., no phoronomic change of the relation of the moved to (empirical) space, it exhibits, nevertheless, a continuous dynamic change of the relation of matter within its space and this change is provable by experience; for instance, there is manifested as an effect of circular motion a constant diminution of the attraction by an endeavor to escape, and thereby circular motion certainly indicates its difference from illusion. One can, for instance, represent the earth as rotated about its axis in infinite empty space and can prove this motion by experience, although neither the relation of the parts of the earth among one another nor their relation to the space outside the earth is changed phoronomically, i.e., in the appearance. For nothing on the earth or in it changes its position with regard to the first space, which is empirical; with reference to the second space, which is completely empty, no external changed relation, and hence no appearance of a motion, can ever occur. However, if I represent to myself a deep hole descending to the center of the earth, and let a stone fall into this hole, but find that although at every distance from the center gravity is always directed thereto yet the falling stone continuously diverges from the vertical direction in its fall, and indeed from west to east; then I conclude that the earth is rotated on its axis from evening to morning. Or if outside I put the stone at some distance from the surface of the earth and the stone does not remain over the same point of the surface but wanders from west to east, then I shall draw the same conclusion as to the aforementioned rotation of the earth on its axis. Either perception[74] is an adequate proof of the actuality of this circular motion, but the change of the earth's relation to external space (the starry heaven) is inadequate inasmuch as this change is a mere appearance which can proceed from two actually opposed causes, and is not a cognition derivable from the ground of explication of all appearances of this change, i.e., from experience. But this motion, even though it is no change of relation to empirical space, is nevertheless no absolute motion but a continuous change of the relations of matters to one another, although it is represented in absolute space and hence is actually only relative motion and, for just this reason alone, is true motion. The fact that this circular motion is true rests upon the representation of the reciprocal continuous withdrawal of each part of the earth (outside of the earth's axis) from every other part that lies *562* at an equal distance from the center of the circle [that is perpendicular to the earth's axis] in the line of this circle's diameter that runs through both of these parts.[75] For this rotation is actual in absolute space inasmuch as by means of this circular motion the withdrawal of the parts at the distance in question, which gravity of itself alone would pull together to one body if there were indeed no dynamical

[74] [That is, the deviation of the stone falling down the hole or falling from a point above the surface of the earth.]

[75] [That is, given a point off the earth's axis of rotation, pass a plane through this point so that this plane is perpendicular to the axis. This plane and the earth's surface intersect in a circle. The "other part" Kant talks about is the point lying opposite the first point in the diameter that runs through the two points and lying at the same distance from the earth's axis (center of the circle) as the first point.]

repulsive cause (as can be seen from the example chosen by Newton in the *Mathematical Principles of Natural Philosophy,* page ten, edition of 1714[76]), is continuously restored; and hence this withdrawal is restored by means of an actual motion referred to the space enclosed within the moved matter (namely, referred to the center of this matter) but not referred to the external space.[77]

As to the case of the third proposition, in order to show the truth of the reciprocally opposed and equal motion of both bodies even without reference to empirical space, there is no need for an active dynamical influence (of gravity or of a stretched string) given through experience, though this was necessary in the case of the second proposition. Rather, there is carried with the mere dynamical possibility of such an influence insofar as this influence is a property of matter (repulsion or attraction)—this very possibility, I say, carries with itself, as regards the motion of the one matter, the equal and opposite motion of the other matter at the same time; and indeed such action and reaction stem from

[76] He there says: *Motus quidem veros corporum singulorum cognoscere et ab apparentibus actu discriminare difficillimum est: propterea, quod partes spatii illius immobilis, in quo corpora vere moventur, non incurrunt in sensus. Causa tamen non est prorsus desperata.** Hereupon he lets two spheres connected by a cord rotate about their common center of gravity in empty space and shows how the actuality of their motion together with its direction can nevertheless be found by experience. I have also tried to show this under somewhat altered circumstances with regard to the earth as moved about its axis.

[77] [That is, the actuality of the earth's rotation rests upon the tendency of the parts of the earth on opposite sides of the axis of rotation to recede from each other. The rotation is actual in absolute space inasmuch as this rotation is referred to the space within, and not to that outside of, the rotating body.]

* ["It is indeed a matter of great difficulty to discover, and effectually to distinguish, the true motions of particular bodies from the apparent; because the parts of that immovable space, in which those motions are performed, do by no means come under the observation of our senses. Yet the thing is not altogether desperate." Florian Cajori's revision of Andrew Motte's translation of 1729 (Berkeley and Los Angeles: University of California Press, 1962), Vol. I, p. 12. Kant must mean, incidentally, the edition of 1713, not 1714. The first edition appeared in 1686, the second in 1713, and the third in 1725–1726.]

mere concepts of a relative motion when this motion is regarded as in absolute space, i.e., according to truth. Therefore, this third proposition is, like everything adequately
provable from mere concepts, a law of an absolutely necessary countermotion.

There is, then, also no absolute motion even if a body in
absolute space is thought of as moved with regard to another body. The motion of both is here not relative to the
space surrounding them but only to the space between them,
which alone determines their external relation to one another, when this space is regarded as absolute; and hence
this motion is again only relative. Absolute motion would,
then, be only that motion which belongs to a body without
a relation to any other matter. Such a motion would be
solely the rectilinear motion of the universe, i.e., of the system of all matter. For if outside of a matter there were still
any other matter, even separated from the former by empty
space, then the motion would certainly be relative. For this
reason, every proof of a law of motion having as its result
the fact that the contrary of this law must imply a rectilinear
motion of the whole universe is an apodeictic proof of the   563
truth of this law, simply because absolute motion would
follow from the contrary of this law, and such motion is
utterly impossible. Of this kind is the law of antagonism in
all community of matter by means of motion. For every
divergence from this law would move the common center
of gravity of all matter, and hence the whole universe, from
its place. On the other hand, this would not happen if one
were to represent the universe as rotated on its axis; therefore, it is always possible to think of such rotation, although
to assume it, as far as one can see, would be quite without
any conceivable use.

The various concepts of empty space also have their
reference to the various concepts of motion and moving
forces. Empty space in a phoronomic respect, also termed
absolute space, should properly not be called empty space.

For it is only the idea of a space in which I abstract from all particular matter (that makes it an object of experience) in order to think in such a space the material, or every empirical, space still as movable, and thereby to think of motion not merely unilaterally as an absolute predicate but always reciprocally as a merely relative one. Such space is, then, nothing at all belonging to the existence of things; but it belongs merely to the determination of concepts, and hence no empty space exists. Empty space in a dynamic respect is that which is not filled, i.e., that in which nothing else movable resists the penetration of the movable, consequently, in which no repulsive force acts. And such space may be either the empty space within the world (*vacuum mundanum*), or, if the world is represented as bounded, then the empty space outside of the world (*vacuum extramundanum*). The empty space within the world may, moreover, be represented either as dispersed (*vacuum disseminatum,* which constitutes only a part of the volume of matter) or as accumulated empty space (*vacuum coacervatum,* which separates bodies, e.g., heavenly bodies, from one another). This distinction is not essential inasmuch as it rests only on the difference of places assigned to empty space in the world; but it is nevertheless used for a distinct purpose: firstly, in order to derive the specific difference of density; secondly, to derive the possibility of a motion in the universe that is free of all external resistance. That it is not necessary to assume empty space for the first purpose has already been shown in the general observation on dynamics;[78] but that empty space is impossible can in no way, from the mere concept of such space, be proved according to the principle of contradiction. However, even if no merely logical ground for its rejection might here be found, there might nevertheless be a general physical ground for banishing it from the doctrine of nature, namely, the ground of the pos-

---

[78] [Cf. above, Ak. 523–525, 532–535.]

sibility of the composition of a matter in general (if such composition were only better comprehended). To this end, let the attraction which is assumed for the explication of the cohesion of matter be only apparent and not true at-   *564* traction—let it be merely the action of compression by means of external matter (the ether) distributed everywhere in the universe. This external matter is itself brought to this pressure only by means of a universal and original attraction, namely, gravitation.[79] This supposition is supported by many reasons, and upon it empty space within matters would be impossible—even if not logically impossible, yet dynamically and hence physically so—because every matter would expand of itself into the empty spaces assumed to be within it (since nothing here resists its expansive force) and would keep these spaces always filled up. An empty space outside of the world would, if by "world" is understood the sum total of all principal attractive matters (the sum total of the large heavenly bodies), be impossible for the very same reasons: namely, according as the distance from these large bodies increases, the attractive force on the ether (which encloses all these bodies and, driven by this attractive force, maintains them in their density by compression) decreases in inverse proportion, and hence this ether itself would only infinitely decrease in density but would nowhere leave the space entirely empty. Nobody need be surprised that this elimination of empty space is in the meantime quite hypothetical; the assertion that there is empty space does not fare any better. Those who venture to decide this controversial question dogmatically, whether they do so affirmatively or negatively, rely ultimately on nothing but metaphysical suppositions, as may be seen in the dynamics; but it was at least necessary to show here that these people cannot at all decide the problem in question. Thirdly, concerning empty space in a mechanical respect, such is the accumulated emptiness

[79] [Cf. above, Ak. 514–515].

within the universe in order to provide the heavenly bodies with free motion. It is easily seen that the possibility or impossibility of such emptiness does not rest on metaphysical grounds but on nature's difficultly disclosed secrets as to why matter sets limits to its own force of extension. Nevertheless, if what was said in the general observation on dynamics as to the possible greater expansion to infinity of specifically different matters with the same quantity of matter (as regards its weight) is granted, then there might indeed be no necessity to assume an empty space for the sake of the free and lasting motion of the heavenly bodies, because the resistance, even in entirely filled spaces, can be thought of as being as small as one wants.

And so ends the metaphysical doctrine of body with the empty and therefore with the inconceivable, wherein this doctrine has the same fate as all other attempts of reason when, in going back to principles, it aspires to the first causes of things. Reason's nature is such that it can never conceive 565 anything except insofar as the latter is determined under given conditions. Consequently, inasmuch as it can neither rest with the conditioned nor make the unconditioned comprehensible, nothing remains for it, when thirst for knowledge invites it to grasp the absolute totality of all conditions, but to turn back from objects to itself in order to investigate and determine the ultimate boundary of the capacity given it, instead of investigating and determining the ultimate boundary of things.[80]

---

[80] [Cf. *Critique of Pure Reason*, B 349–398.]

The Unity
of Kant's Thought
in His Philosophy
of Corporeal Nature

INTRODUCTION

In Kant's Preface to the *Metaphysical Foundations of Natural Science,* he claims that this metaphysics of corporeal nature can be presented as a complete system "inasmuch as the object [matter] must . . . be compared with all the necessary laws of thought [and so this metaphysics] must furnish a definite number of cognitions, which can be fully exhausted."[1] The table of categories to be found in the early part of the *Critique of Pure Reason* provides the schema for the elaboration of this metaphysical system of corporeal nature.[2]

Quite obviously Kant takes his architectonic very seriously, and consequently the reader of the *Metaphysical Foundations of Natural Science* cannot understand in the fullest sense what is going on in that treatise unless he is also familiar with the "Transcendental Analytic" of the *Critique of Pure Reason.* Kant develops his system of corporeal nature in the following way. He starts in the *Critique* with the most formal act of human cognition, called by him the transcendental unity of apperception, and its various aspects, called the logical functions of judgment. He then proceeds to the pure categories of the understanding, and then to the schematized categories, and finally to the transcendental principles of

[1] Above, Ak. 473. References to the translation will be made to the (marginal) Akademie edition page numbers.

[2] See above, Ak. 474–476: "Under the four classes of quantity, quality, relation, and finally modality, all determinations of the universal concept of a matter in general and, therefore, everything that can be thought a priori respecting it, that can be presented in mathematical construction, or that can be given in experience as a determinate object of experience, must be capable of being brought. There is no more to do in the way of discovery or addition. . . ."

nature in general. In the *Metaphysical Foundations* he is at long last ready to consider the metaphysical principles of corporeal nature. There is a progression from what is most formal (and so least empirical) to what is less formal (and so more empirical). The *Metaphysical Foundations* is, therefore, a subsequent stage of an elaborate architectonic. The present essay is intended to show how the metaphysics of corporeal nature fits into this grand architectonic scheme, and I must accordingly spend more time talking about the *Critique* than the *Metaphysical Foundations*. I must assume, therefore, that the reader is familiar with both treatises; if he is not, then this essay will not be very enlightening.

As mentioned above, Kant takes his architectonic quite seriously (though many of his commentators do not). Unfortunately, he did not always make clear how the gears of this grand machine mesh (perhaps one reason why so many of his commentators do not take it seriously). In the following essay I shall try to make clear the workings of this architectonic, which is the very core of Kant's philosophy of corporeal nature. If my efforts are blessed with even moderate success, this essay will have some excuse for being.

Few if any philosophers have excited so much comment—both favorable and unfavorable—as has Kant. Even among those critics who profess a great admiration and respect for Kant's efforts, often many reservations are expressed. "Like all great pioneering works in philosophy the *Critique* is full of mistakes and confusions. It is a misunderstanding to think that a supreme philosopher cannot have erred badly and often: the *Critique* still has much to teach us, but it is wrong on nearly every page."[3] It is difficult to see how a man who supposedly has made so many mistakes and been the victim of so much confusion could be worthy of any respect or admiration at all. It may be, of course, that much of the con-

[3] Jonathan Bennett, *Kant's Analytic* (Cambridge: Cambridge University Press, 1966), p. viii.

fusion lies in the critic's mind; if so, then Kant is vindicated.

With regard to Kant's confusion specifically in his architectonic and the role the categories are supposed to play in that architectonic, Schopenhauer speaks out quite boldly when he says that the

> table of categories is now supposed to be the guiding line along which every metaphysical, and in fact every scientific, speculation is to be conducted (*Prolegomena*, §39). In fact, it is not only the foundation of the whole Kantian philosophy, and the type according to which its symmetry is carried through everywhere, as I have already shown above, but it has also really become the Procrustean bed on to which Kant forces every possible consideration by means of a violence that I shall now consider somewhat more closely. . . . But in every inquiry conducted by Kant, every quantity in time and space, and every possible quality of things, physical, moral, and so on, is brought under those category-titles, although between these things and those titles of the forms of judging and thinking there is not the least thing in common, except the accidental and arbitrary nomenclature. We must be mindful of the high esteem due to Kant in other respects, in order not to express our indignation at this procedure in harsh terms. The pure physiological table of general principles of natural science at once furnishes us with the nearest example. What in the world has the quantity of judgements to do with the fact that every perception has an extensive magnitude? What has the quality of judgements to do with the fact that every sensation has a degree? On the contrary, the former rests on the fact that space is the form of our external perception, and the latter is nothing more than an empirical, and moreover quite subjective, observation or perception drawn merely from the consideration of the nature of our sense-organs. . . . Several examples, if possible even more glaring, are furnished by the table of the *categories of freedom* in the *Critique of Practical Reason;* further by the *Critique of Judgement,* first book, which goes through the judgement of taste according to the four titles of the categories; finally by the *Metaphysical Rudiments [Foundations] of Natural Science* which are cut out entirely in accordance with the table of categories. Possibly the false, which is mixed up here and there with what is true and excellent in this important work, was mainly brought about precisely in this way. Let us see,

at the end of the first chapter [of the *Metaphysical Founda-tions*], how the unity, plurality, and totality of the directions of lines are supposed to correspond to the categories, so named according to the quantity of the judgements.[4]

Aware of all these rumblings, I embark on this voyage to explore the workings of Kant's architectonic not without some trepidation.

I. THE TRANSCENDENTAL UNITY OF APPERCEPTION

Kant maintains that the "synthetic unity of apperception is therefore that highest point, to which we must ascribe all employment of the understanding, even the whole of logic, and comformably therewith, transcendental philosophy. Indeed this faculty of apperception is the understanding itself."[5] He very likely took the rather high-sounding term "apperception" from Leibniz;[6] it means consciousness. Kant thus holds consciousness to be the very beginning of all speculative philosophy, just as Descartes held the *cogito* in his *Meditations*. Now, the representations contained in consciousness can be viewed in two ways, as merely the contents of our consciousness, or as referring beyond themselves to the objects which they purport to represent.

[4] *The World as Will and Representation,* trans. E. F. J. Payne (Indian Hills, Colorado: The Falcon's Wing Press, 1958), Vol. I, pp. 470–471.

[5] *Critique of Pure Reason,* trans. Norman Kemp Smith (London: Macmillan and Co., 1929, and St. Martin's Press: New York, 1964), B 134 note, p. 154. This and the following quotations from the *Critique* are printed by permission of St. Martin's Press. Page numbers refer to their paperback edition.

[6] Leibniz says, "Thus it is well to make distinction between the perception, which is the inner state of the monad representing external things, and apperception, which is consciousness or the reflective knowledge of this inner state; the latter not being given to all souls, nor at all times to the same soul." "Principles of Nature and of Grace, Based on Reason," published 1714, in *Leibniz Selections,* ed. Philip P. Wiener (New York: Charles Scribner's Sons, 1951), p. 525.

According to the first way it "must be possible for the 'I think' to accompany all my representations; for otherwise something would be represented in me which could not be thought at all, and that is equivalent to saying that the representation would be impossible, or at least would be nothing to me."[7] Thus he asserts the unity of consciousness—that all my representations are bound up together as the thoughts of one mind.[8] This pure apperception is an act of spontaneity and as such is different from sensibility, which is a passive receptivity for intuitions. This means that the representation "I think" is simple and in itself entirely empty of any content. No manifold is given through the "I think"; rather, every manifold is given to the "I think" to be determined. Accordingly, we do not know our noumenal selves, as Kant claims Descartes taught. Rather, the self

is known only through the thoughts which are its predicates, and of it, apart from them, we cannot have any concept whatsoever, but can only revolve in a perpetual circle, since any judgment upon it has always already made use of its representation. And the reason why this inconvenience is inseparably bound up with it, is that consciousness in itself is not a representation distinguishing a particular object, but a form of representation in general, that is, of representation in so far as it is to be entitled knowledge; for it is only of knowledge that I can say that I am thereby thinking something.[9]

This is to say that the self becomes aware of itself and gains cognition of itself only by bringing to self-consciousness (through an act of synthesis) the manifold of intuitions afforded by sensibility. Accordingly, the self knows itself only phenomenally.

[7] *Critique of Pure Reason,* B 131–132, pp. 152–153.

[8] Cf. *ibid.,* B 132, p. 153: "For the manifold representations, which are given in an intuition, would not be one and all *my* representations, if they did not all belong to one self-consciousness. As *my* representations (even if I am not conscious of them as such) they must conform to the condition under which alone they *can* stand together in one universal self-consciousness. . . ."

[9] *Ibid.,* B 404, pp. 331–332.

In the second place, representations refer beyond themselves to the objects which they purport to represent. Although human apperception is spontaneous, it is not creative. A creative (or intuitive) understanding would be one
which could through its self-consciousness supply to itself
the manifold of intuition.[10] Such an understanding would
create the objects of its representations through its own self-
consciousness. The human understanding does not intuit; it
synthesizes the manifold which sensibility intuits. Indeed
synthesizing the manifold of sensible intuition is exactly what
is meant by saying that apperception is an act of spontaneity.
For the moment, let us say that such synthesizing activity of
the mind means that unity can be bestowed upon a manifold
of perceptions by the mind's going through that manifold,
taking it up, and connecting it according to a concept which
serves as a rule. For example, the concept of cause and effect
can serve as a rule for synthesizing a manifold, e.g., the
perceptions involved in observing a stove's heating a room.
I shall have much more to say about synthesis later on when
the logical forms of judgment and the categories are treated.

The two preceding paragraphs have spoken of two unities.
Let us call the unity treated in the first the subjective unity of
consciousness, and that treated in the second the objective
unity of consciousness. Actually these two unities are merely
two sides of the same synthetic unity of representations. Kant
states that the principle of the subjective unity of consciousness "is itself, indeed, an identical, and therefore analytic,
proposition. . . ."[11] This principle merely says that all my
representations are my representations. Correlatively, let us
ask how it is that the consciousness of given representations
can determine in a definite way the thoroughgoing unity of
self-consciousness in the consciousness of my representations. The answer is that I think this or that. Only thus do I

[10] Cf. *ibid.*, B 138–139.

[11] *Ibid.*, B 135, pp. 154–155.

have a determinate thought. My thinking is differentiated by objects. And so the necessity of a relationship of my representations to objects is expressed in the "I think". The analytic principle of the subjective unity of thought "nevertheless . . . reveals the necessity of a synthesis of the manifold given in intuition, without which the thoroughgoing identity of self-consciousness cannot be thought. For through the 'I', as simple representation, nothing manifold is given; only in intuition, which is distinct from the 'I', can a manifold be given; and only through *combination* in one consciousness can it be thought."[12] And so the subjective unity of consciousness expresses an objective unity of consciousness. The "I think" synthesizes a given manifold of intuition to yield cognition of an object. For obvious reasons, Kant sometimes calls the objective unity of self-consciousness the synthetic unity of self-consciousness.

I mentioned earlier (p. 142) that the human understanding is not intuitive; it is discursive by means of concepts.[13] We do not know objects immediately; we cognize objects mediately through concepts. A concept is the consciousness of the determinate relationship of given representations to an object; and in this concept the manifold of given representations is united, e.g., the concept "horse" applies to Bucephalus.[14] Kant calls the operation by which given representations (e.g., spruce, willow, linden) are transformed into

[12] *Ibid.*, B 135, p. 155.

[13] Cf. *ibid.*, B 92–93, p. 105: "The understanding has thus far been explained merely negatively, as a non-sensible faculty of knowledge. Now since without sensibility we cannot have any intuition, understanding cannot be a faculty of intuition. But besides intuition there is no other mode of knowledge except by means of concepts. The knowledge yielded by understanding, or at least by the human understanding, must therefore be by means of concepts, and so is not intuitive, but discursive."

[14] Cf. *ibid.*, B 93, p. 105: "Whereas all intuitions, as sensible, rest on affections, concepts rest on functions. By 'function' I mean the unity of the act of bringing various representations under one common representation. Concepts are based on the spontaneity of thought, sensible intuitions on the receptivity of impressions."

a concept (e.g., tree) an analytic one; the form (universality) of a concept arises analytically; the specific unity of representations that is thought in the concept is an analytic unity.[15] And so we have not only a synthetic unity of consciousness but also an analytic unity of consciousness. The analytic unity presupposes the synthetic.

> The analytic unity of consciousness belongs to all general concepts, as such. If, for instance, I think red in general, I thereby represent to myself a property which (as a characteristic) can be found in something, or can be combined with other representations; that is, only by means of a presupposed possible synthetic unity can I represent to myself the analytic unity. A representation which is to be thought as common to *different* representations is regarded as belonging to such as have, in addition to it, also something *different*. Consequently it must previously be thought in synthetic unity with other (though, it may be, only possible) representations, before I can think in it the analytic unity of consciousness, which makes it a *conceptus communis*.[16]

In contrast to our discursive understandings we can (at least problematically) think of an intuitive understanding.

> It is, in fact, a distinctive characteristic of our understanding, that in its cognition . . . it moves from the *analytic universal* to the particular, or, in other words, from conceptions to given empirical intuitions. In this process, therefore, it determines nothing in respect of the multiplicity of the particular. . . . But now we are also able to form a notion of an understanding which, not being discursive like ours, but intuitive, moves from the *synthetic universal,* or intuition of a whole as a whole, to the particular—that is to say, from the whole to the parts.[17]

And so Kant distinguishes an analytic universal concept, which is discursive, from a thinkable synthetic universal concept, which is intuitive. The latter concept is the intuition of a whole as a whole; the necessary correlate of such a concept

[15] Cf. *ibid.,* B 102.

[16] *Ibid.,* B 133–134 note, p. 154.

[17] *Critique of Teleological Judgement,* trans. J. C. Meredith (Oxford: Oxford University Press, 1928), p. 63 (Ak. 407).

is not our discursive concept of an object in general (which is a simple and entirely contentless representation), but is the intuition of the totality of objects. In our discursive cognition by means of universal concepts our self-consciousness is not related to the whole of the manifold of representations (the totality of objects) collectively, but is related only to an object in general, and hence to the totality of objects merely distributively.

And so a discursive concept (*conceptus communis*) is at the same time both a universal representation and a representation of a part—it is not a universal representation insofar as it is the representation of a whole as a whole. This means that all our concepts are marks, or partial representations; and as such they are analytic grounds of cognition. To say that a concept is a partial representation involves what is meant when a concept is said to have a content; to say that it is an analytic ground of cognition involves what is meant when it is said to have a range (or sphere). Content and range are inversely proportional. The concept with the widest range is that of an object in general, i.e., gold, silver, metal, movable thing, and everything else fall under it. But it has no content, i.e., it represents no given thing. The concept of gold has a narrower range, but it has more content. Concepts are subordinated to one another according to their increasing ranges (or decreasing contents), e.g., gold, metal, movable thing, object in general. Inasmuch as all concepts are general, they only partially represent particular objects. Intuitions are particular and immediately related to individual things.[18]

We now know what the objective unity of self-consciousness is and what a concept in general (i.e., the analytic unity of consciousness) is. And we know that analysis presupposes

[18] Cf. *Critique of Pure Reason*, B 93, p. 105: "Since no representation, save when it is an intuition, is in immediate relation to an object, no concept is ever related to an object immediately, but to some other representation of it, be that other representation an intuition, or itself a concept."

synthesis. Concepts are made by analysis, but prior to any such analysis there must be a synthetic activity of the mind. This act of synthesis is judging. And so judgment, rather than conception, is the fundamental activity of the mind; indeed Kant regards concepts as predicates of possible judgments.[19] He explains a judgment as the "manner in which given modes of knowledge [*Erkenntnisse*] are brought to the objective unity of apperception."[20]

Such objective unity of given representations is to be contrasted with a subjective unity of representations. The former is necessary insofar as knowledge is to be acquired by means of the relation of the given representations.

> Only in this way does there arise from this relation a *judgment,* that is, a relation which is *objectively valid,* and so can be adequately distinguished from a relation of the same representations that would have only subjective validity—as when they are connected according to laws of association. In the latter case, all that I could say would be, 'If I support a body, I feel an impression of weight'; I could not say, 'It, the body, is heavy'. Thus to say 'The body is heavy' is not merely to state that the two representations have always been conjoined in my perception, however often that perception be repeated; what we are asserting is that they are combined *in the object,* no matter what the state of the subject may be.[21]

To say that a judgment is objectively valid is to say that it is true, i.e., representations are so related in a judgment that

---

[19] Cf. *ibid.,* B 94, p. 106: "Now we can reduce all acts of the understanding to judgments, and the *understanding* may therefore be represented as a *faculty of judgment.* For, as stated above, the understanding is a faculty of thought. Thought is knowledge by means of concepts. But concepts, as predicates of possible judgments, relate to some representation of a not yet determined object. Thus the concept of body means something, for instance, metal, which can be known by means of that concept. It is therefore a concept solely in virtue of its comprehending other representations, by means of which it can relate to objects. It is therefore the predicate of a possible judgment, for instance, 'every metal is a body'."

[20] *Ibid.,* B 141, p. 159.

[21] *Ibid.,* B 142, p. 159.

this relation is ontologically valid and thus true of things.

One must note that the logical form of *every* judgment consists in the original synthetic unity of apperception. The content, or matter, of a judgment consists in the representations to be related to one another in the judgment. The form of the judgment consists in the way these given representations are related to one another in the objective unity of apperception. According to content a judgment may be either analytic or synthetic, depending on whether the predicate-concept is. something which is already thought in the subject-concept, or the predicate-concept is indeed somehow connected with the subject-concept but not contained in it (e.g., "All bodies are extended" is analytic, while "All bodies are heavy" is synthetic). But according to logical form, even the form of an analytic judgment consists in the synthetic unity of apperception.[22] This refutes those commentators who have emphatically claimed that the form of an analytic judgment consists in the analytic unity of consciousness and the form of a synthetic judgment in the synthetic unity of consciousness. Kant *says* that the distinction between analytic and synthetic judgments is a question of the *content* of the judgments, while the *form* of both kinds of judgments consists in the synthetic unity of apperception. Indeed the "synthetic unity of apperception is therefore that highest point, to which we must ascribe all employment of the understanding, even the whole of logic, and conformably therewith, transcendental philosophy. Indeed this faculty of apperception is the understanding itself."[23]

---

[22] Cf. *ibid.*, B 131 note, p. 152: "Whether the representations are in themselves identical, and whether, therefore, one can be analytically thought through the other, is not a question that here arises. The *consciousness* of the one, when the manifold is under consideration, has always to be distinguished from the consciousness of the other; and it is with the synthesis of this (possible) consciousness that we are here alone concerned." Cf. also *Prolegomena*, §2, Ak. 266.

[23] *Ibid.*, B 134 note, p. 154.

II. THE LOGICAL FORMS OF JUDGMENT

The logical form of a judgment consists in the way that the given representations are combined in the synthetic unity of apperception. What are the various ways in which the given representations are so combined? This, of course, is a question of the famous table of the logical functions of judgment and especially of that table's completeness—one of the thorniest problems in all of Kant's philosophy. It is of the utmost importance in our consideration of the architectonic, because the completeness of the table of categories depends entirely upon the completeness of the table of logical functions. Where did Kant get this table and can it lay any claim at all to completeness? Unfortunately, Kant himself gives us very little direct help in the *Critique of Pure Reason;* we shall see why at the end of this Part Two. One must search through the unpublished manuscripts on logic and metaphysics found after his death (*Der handschriftliche Nachlaß* of the Academy edition), and through the notes taken on his lectures (which have just appeared in the Academy edition). Also, this search must be guided by a great deal of *Kantgefühl.*

In the first half of this Part Two let us consider the question of where the table comes from; in the last half, the question of the table's completeness. The answer usually given to the first question is that Kant gleaned the table empirically from the logic textbooks in use at his time.[24] This is undoubtedly

[24] Kant does say, "But in order to discover such a principle, I looked about for an act of the understanding which comprises all the rest and is distinguished only by various modifications or phases, in reducing the multiplicity of representation to the unity of thinking in general. I found this act of the understanding to consist in judging. Here, then, the labors of the logicians were ready at hand, though not yet quite free from defects; and with this help I was enabled to exhibit a complete table of the pure functions of the understanding, which are however undetermined with respect to any object.

the way in which he first became aware of the separate
logical forms. But the logic books he might have been famil-

I finally referred these functions of judging to objects in general, or rather
to the condition of determining judgments as objectively valid; and so there
arose the pure concepts of the understanding, concerning which I could make
certain that these, and this exact number only, constitute our whole knowledge
of things by pure understanding." *Prolegomena to Any Future Metaphysics,*
Mahaffy-Carus translation extensively revised by Lewis White Beck (The
Library of Liberal Arts, New York: Bobbs-Merrill, 1950), p. 71 (Ak. 323). But
this hardly amounts to a confession that he raked the list together haphazardly
without following any a priori principle. Cf. Hegel, *Encyclopaedia of the
Philosophical Sciences,* Part I, The Science of Logic, trans. William Wallace
(Oxford: Oxford University Press, 1892), p. 87: "Kant, it is well known, did
not put himself to much trouble in discovering the categories. 'I', the unity of
self-consciousness, being quite abstract and completely indeterminate, the
question arises, how are we to get at the specialized forms of the 'I', the
categories? Fortunately, the common logic offers to our hand an empirical
classification of the kinds of *judgment.* Now, to judge is the same thing as to
think of a determinate object. Hence the various modes of judgment, as
enumerated to our hand, provide us with the several categories of thought."
Even a sympathetic critic like Wilhelm Windelband finds serious problems.
Compare his "The Principles of Logic," trans. Ethel Meyer, in *Encyclopaedia
of the Philosophical Sciences,* eds. William Windelband and Arnold Ruge, Vol.
I (London: Macmillan and Co., 1913), p. 29: "But we arrive at the same result
through a criticism of the division of judgments as they were taken over
by Kant in his well-known table as the result of the dogmatic structure of
Formal Logic. Since the investigations of Sigwart and Lotze, however, it
can no longer pretend to be obviously true, as it did in the last century."
Also *ibid.,* p. 40 note: "We must not, therefore, reproach Kant because he
sought in the relation of the categories to the kinds of judgment a ground
of common principles for the two parts of his Logic—the formal and the
transcendental: we must hold firmly to the inner connexion between the
two. The defect of the 'transcendental analytic' is only that the 'table of
categories' is 'raked together' entirely historically. For the division is neither
derived nor derivable from the essence of the judgment, but was taken over
empirically from the scholastic Logic and trimmed up into a symmetrical
trichotomy." Cf. also Josiah Royce, *Lectures on Modern Idealism* (New Haven:
Yale University Press, 1919), p. 47: ". . . [Kant] obtained his table of the
categories of the understanding in a somewhat more superficial way, viz.,
from a consideration of the traditional classification of judgments that the textbooks of formal logic contained. In any case, his list of the forms essential
to our intelligence looks rather empirical. He gives us no reason why just
these forms and no others *must* result from the very nature of a self such as
ours. No one principle seems to define the whole list. His forms appear in
his account without any statement of their genesis and with no acceptable
discussion of the reasons for holding his list to be exhaustive."

iar with present grounds for various possible lists, and the question is why he chose the list he did rather than some other one. A person with nothing more than a little bit of *Kantgefühl* would doubtless hazard the guess that Kant's reasons for choosing his list are a priori rather than a posteriori.

I thought about this problem for many years, and reading widely in the commentaries—Vaihinger, Smith, de Vleeschauwer, Paton, et alia—gained no satisfactory answers. Finally Klaus Reich's *Die Vollständigkeit der kantischen Urteilstafel* (*The Completeness of the Kantian Table of Judgments*, Berlin: Richard Schoetz, 1932), came to my attention. It was like walking into a brightly lighted room, if I may say of this what Goethe is reputed to have said about the *Critique of Pure Reason*. All the pieces of the puzzle fell into place. Through Reich's help I have come as close as I shall very likely ever be to the very truth itself regarding this thorny problem in Kant's philosophy. In this Part Two, therefore, I shall draw freely on Reich's work, and can obviously make no claim to originality here. But the truth should be the property of all men. In what ensues I have made no effort to follow the exact order of Reich's arguments, but have drawn on his book freely as suits my purposes at this stage of our exploration of Kant's architectonic.

Where does the list come from? Its origins are a priori inasmuch as it can be shown to follow analytically from the above-mentioned explication of a judgment in general (p. 146). A judgment relates representations in such a way that the relation is ontologically valid and, accordingly, true of things. This characteristic of a judgment is its modality. We relate representations in such a way that this relationship is thought of as being objectively valid.[25] However, it will be

[25] Cf. *Critique of Pure Reason,* B 99–100, p. 109: "The *modality* of judgments is a quite peculiar function. Its distinguishing characteristic is that it contributes nothing to the content of the judgment . . . but concerns only the value of the copula in relation to thought in general."

more convenient in enumerating the various logical functions of thought to begin with the categorical form of relation. We shall see later (p. 165) that the modal forms and
the relational ones are intertwined, and so we may exercise
an option here. Mindful of the fact that modality is the very
first characteristic of our explication of a judgment in general, let us nevertheless first try to see how the categorical
form is contained in our explication. The convenience in so
beginning will become apparent as the various functions
issue forth from our explication.

Concepts are the given materials that are brought together
in the objective unity of apperception.[26] Our explication says
that given concepts are united in a judgment in such a way
that they stand in relation to original pure apperception and
its necessary unity. This means that the given concepts must
be so related to one another that they represent an object.
Kant calls this the *relation* of a judgment.

We saw earlier (p. 145) that concepts taken in themselves have an analytic relationship to one another. This is
their subordination, e.g., gold, metal, body, object in general.
Every judgment involves this relationship simply because
concepts are the matter of judgments. But this is not the relationship according to which concepts are combined in the
transcendental unity of apperception to yield knowledge of
objects. A concept taken in itself is entirely general; the concept "tree" represents what is common to an oak, beech,
linden, etc.—namely, an object having roots, trunk, branches,
leaves—and it is just for this very reason that "tree" can represent not only oak, beech, linden but larch, birch, spruce,
etc. as well. The application of a concept has to be determined in such a way as to give us definite knowledge. By itself
a concept swims in the vast ocean of possibility. How can it
be fixed in order to yield some actual cognition of objects?

[26] Cf. *ibid.*, B 322, p. 280: "In any judgment we can call the given concepts
logical matter (i.e., matter for the judgment), and their relation (by means of
the copula) the form of the judgment."

We have just seen in the preceding paragraph that concepts are the only materials we have for the act of judging. Therefore, in order for a judgment to be made, concepts must be subordinated in such a way that they can be thought of as belonging together so as to represent an object. As far as the analytic subordination of concepts is concerned, the only requirement is that the range of one concept be contained in the range of another—i.e., gold, metal; but not metal, gold. The synthetic requirements for objective knowledge presuppose this analytic subordination, to be sure; but there is a further demand that the concepts be subordinated in such a way as to give cognition of an object (or objects). In other words, one concept must be thought of as the condition of the application of another in order that we may acquire objective knowledge, e.g., all oaks are trees (the application of "tree" is conditioned by "oak"). The concept serving as the condition has the function of the subject, while the other has the function of the predicate—i.e., S is P. Such a synthesis of two given concepts is called the function of the *categorical* judgment.

Let us now consider briefly how this account of the categorical judgment meets the restriction of pure general logic that only the form of knowledge be treated and not the content.[27] The formal unity of a judgment in general is the objective unity of consciousness. Since concepts of themselves do not provide us with knowledge of things, their objective employment is possible only on the supposition that certain given concepts are to be related in the objective unity of consciousness. What is the condition for the objective employment of concepts? A concept taken in itself expresses nothing more than the analytic unity in the consciousness of my representations. A concept so taken is completely

[27] Cf. *ibid.*, B 79, p. 95: "General logic . . . abstracts from all content of knowledge . . . and considers only the logical form in the relation of any knowledge to other knowledge; that is, it treats of the form of thought in general."

indeterminate as regards its objective reference. Accordingly, the analytic unity of consciousness expressed by the form of a concept (see pp. 143–144, above) does not have objective validity. What imparts this objective validity to a concept? It is the presence of another concept that specifies a *condition* for the former concept's application, as a predicate to a subject or the application of a rule to what is subsumed under it. We have come to this notion of the condition of a judgment *analytically* by considering nothing but the form of a judgment in general (its objective validity) and the form of a concept in general (which does not by itself have objective validity). If a concept is to function in such a way as to make a judgment possible, then it must acquire objective validity. Such validity is acquired when a condition for its application is supplied; this purely formal requirement therefore properly belongs to pure general logic since it borrows nothing from the matter (or content) of thought. And so the function of the categorical judgment is already present in the form of a judgment in general.

Two given concepts cannot be related so as to have objective validity by any function of judgment other than the categorical. But now after gaining the categorical function of judgment, we have not only concepts but also categorical judgments as possible matter for other functions of judgment. Can two categorical judgments be related in apperception in such a way as to give us further objective knowledge? We can at least have many truths (objectively valid categorical judgments), for such judgments can be conjoined (e.g., "There is a perfect justice and the obstinately wicked are punished"); but as far as the objective unity of consciousness is concerned, the conjunction is merely additive (i.e., one can just as easily say, "The obstinately wicked are punished and there is a perfect justice"). Such a conjunction involves no new form of knowledge and so is not another form of judgment. Similarly, a disjunction of categorical judgments involves no new form of knowledge unless the disjunction is such that its components determine the totality of some knowledge, as we shall see later (pp. 156–158). Now, the form of a judgment in general involves a *thorough-going* objective unity of apperception in the consciousness of my representations.[28] If we have nothing but categorical judgments, then it will be impossible for us to have truth taken formally as the reference of given thoughts (either concepts or judgments) to the thoroughgoing unity of objective consciousness. Since this "principle of apperception is the highest principle in the whole sphere of human knowledge,"[29] we may therefore conclude that distinct categorical judgments must admit of combination in an objective unity of their consciousness.

How are such judgments to be combined? Very much like the way in which two concepts (the one serving as the subject and the other as the predicate) were related to one another through the categorical form of thought so as to constitute truth. In the present case one judgment may be the condition for using the other one in such a way as to attain possible truth, i.e., the one may be the condition of the actual reference of the other to an objective situation. In such a relationship of categorical propositions, it makes a great deal of difference whether I say, "If there is a perfect justice, then the obstinately wicked are punished", or say, "If the obstinately wicked are punished, then there is a perfect justice". When our two categorical judgments are so combined in the objective unity of consciousness, they serve as the mat-

[28] Cf. *ibid.*, B 133–135, pp. 153–155: "This thoroughgoing identity of the apperception of a manifold which is given in intuition contains a synthesis of representations, and is possible only through the consciousness of this synthesis. . . . This principle of the necessary unity of apperception . . . reveals the necessity of a synthesis of the manifold given in intuition, without which the thoroughgoing identity of self-consciousness cannot be thought. For through the 'I', as simple representation, nothing manifold is given; only in intuition, which is distinct from the 'I', can a manifold be given; and only through *combination* in one consciousness can it be thought."

[29] *Ibid.*, B 135, p. 154.

ter for a new form of judgment. Since logic abstracts from the content of knowledge and considers only the form of thought, we must abstract from the fact that the constituent concepts of the two judgments have already been referred to apperception through the categorical function of thought. This means that the truth of both categorical judgments is here left undecided except as it is conditioned by their connection in the new judgment.[30] This connection is the function of the *hypothetical* judgment, which is expressed by "if . . . , then . . .". The one categorical judgment serving as the condition has the function of the antecedent, and the other has the function of the consequence.

We have just seen that in the case of the hypothetical judgment the relationship of concepts thought in the constituent categorical judgments is left undetermined as regards objective validity (truth) because of the requirements of formal logic. The thought of leaving objective validity undetermined is necessary (through the function of the categorical judgment) for the form of truth in general. Initially we discerned the objective validity of a relationship of concepts in the categorical judgment. The form of a judgment in general then required a relationship no longer merely of concepts but of judgments. This function of the hypothetical judgment did make objective knowledge possible, i.e., the logical sequence was true. But this fact implies that it must be possible to leave the truth of the constituent categorical judgments undetermined. A (categorical) judgment thought in this form is called a *problematic* judgment.

At first glance the notion of a problematic judgment might strike one as being a bit strange. From the explication of a

---

[30] Cf. *ibid.*, B 98–99, p. 109: "The hypothetical proposition, 'If there is a perfect justice, the obstinately wicked are punished', really contains the relation of two propositions, namely, 'There is a perfect justice', and 'The obstinately wicked are punished'. Whether both these propositions are in themselves true, here remains undetermined. It is only the logical sequence which is thought by this judgment."

judgment in general as a synthesis of representations in the transcendental unity of apperception, it might seem that any judgment ought to be an objectively valid synthesis of representations. But through the problematic function of thought nothing is "judged"; by the very form of this function the truth of a connection of representations is left undetermined. The connection between subject and predicate as expressed in a problematic categorical judgment is only subjectively valid. But we have just seen from our consideration of the hypothetical judgment that the problematic function of thought does necessarily belong to the form of a judgment in general. And so we must conclude that such problematic validity of a connection of subject and predicate must have a determinate relationship to the objective validity of this connection in the form of judging in general—i.e., there must be some function of thought that determines the truth or falsity of a problematic judgment. We shall see next what this function is.

By itself the problematic function of thought leaves truth undecided. We have seen above that the hypothetical function of thought can bestow objective validity on the connection of two such judgments.[31] But this function says nothing about the truth or falsity of the single problematic judgments (serving as the logical matter for the hypothetical one) when they are considered in themselves; this function tells us only that the antecedent can be false without the consequence having to be so, and that the consequence can be true without the antecedent having to be so. There must be a special function of thought that determines the objective validity of

[31] Cf. *ibid.*, B 100, p. 110: "Thus the two judgments, the relation of which constitutes the hypothetical judgment (*antecedens et consequens*) . . . are one and all problematic only. In the above example ['If there is a perfect justice, the obstinately wicked are punished'], the proposition, 'There is a perfect justice', is not stated assertorically, but is thought only as an optional judgment, which it is possible to assume; it is only the logical sequence which is assertoric. Such judgments may therefore be obviously false, and yet, taken problematically, may be conditions of the knowledge of truth."

the single problematic judgment inasmuch as arbitrary prob-lematic judgments do not of themselves determine anything more than their subjective validity. This function cannot be something lying outside of the given problematic judgments; for it must be what first refers the given problematic judg-ments as such to the objective unity of apperception, since a judgment in general is explained as the way in which given representations (concepts) or thoughts (judgments) are brought to the objective unity of consciousness. This is to say that the required function must follow analytically from the form of a judgment in general. And so the given prob-lematic judgments must themselves constitute this function. In their totality (in community) must they determine the truth. Since no part of this totality is given in itself as true, they must reciprocally determine one another in such a way that the truth is thereby determined.

The *disjunctive* function of thought (expressed by means of the "either . . . or") conjoins its constituent problematic judgments in just such a reciprocally determinant objectively valid relationship.[32] The sense of the disjunction is that one of the parts is true without a definite one of the parts being thought as true, as will be shown in detail on pp. 160–162, be-low. The parts determining the totality of the knowledge are what is conditioned in this relationship; the totality (whole) determined through the parts is the condition.[33] The disjunc-

[32] Cf. *ibid.,* B 100–101, p. 110: "[The] judgments the reciprocal relation of which forms the disjunctive judgment (members of the division), are one and all problematic only. . . . Thus the judgment, 'The world exists by blind chance [or through inner necessity, or through an external cause]', has in the disjunctive judgment only problematic meaning, namely, as a proposition that may for a moment be assumed."

[33] Cf. *ibid.,* B 99, p. 109: "Finally, the disjunctive judgment contains a relation of two or more propositions to each other, a relation not, however, of logical sequence [as in the hypothetical judgment], but of logical opposi-tion, in so far as the sphere of the one excludes the sphere of the other, and yet at the same time of community, in so far as the propositions taken to-gether occupy the whole sphere of the knowledge in question. The disjunctive judgment expresses, therefore, a relation of the parts of the sphere of such

tion consists in the unity of the conditioned and its condition as regards the use of merely problematically given judgments as such so as to attain objective knowledge. We now have the three *relational* moments of thought: subject-predicate, antecedent-consequence, and whole-parts.

As Kant says in the last footnote, the constituent problematic judgments are thought of in such a way that, since the sphere of each part is a complement of the sphere of the others, they determine the true knowledge when they are taken together. But this means that this connection of merely problematic judgments determines some one of them as being objectively valid (true). In Kant's example, "The world exists through blind chance, or through inner necessity, or through an external cause", one of the constituent judgments must be true, though the disjunction certainly does not tell us which one.[34] Since we have derived the form of the disjunctive judgment analytically from the form of judging in general, it is quite clear that we have gained another function of thought—namely, the *necessity* of a judgment. In the disjunctive function one of the members thereby related must be true; logical necessity is, then, the objective

---

knowledge, since the sphere of each part is a complement of the sphere of the others, yielding together the sum-total of the divided knowledge. Take, for instance, the judgment, 'The world exists through blind chance, or through inner necessity, or through an external cause'. Each of these propositions occupies a part of the sphere of the possible knowledge concerning the existence of a world in general; all of them together occupy the whole sphere. To take the knowledge out of one of these spheres means placing it in one of the other spheres, and to place it in one sphere means taking it out of the others. There is, therefore, in a disjunctive judgment a certain community of the known constituents, such that they mutually exclude each other, and yet thereby determine *in their totality* the true knowledge. For, when taken together, they constitute the whole content of one given knowledge."

[34] Cf. *ibid.*, B 100–101, p. 110: "Thus the judgment, 'The world exists by blind chance', has in the disjunctive judgment only problematic meaning, namely, as a proposition that may for a moment be assumed. At the same time, like the indication of a false road among the number of all those roads that can be taken, it aids in the discovery of the true proposition."

validity which is assumed with the merely problematic validity under given conditions.

Necessary validity, actual validity, and problematic validity comprise the *modal* moments of thought. "The *modality* of judgments is a quite peculiar function. Its distinguishing characteristic is that it contributes nothing to the content of the judgment . . . but concerns only the value of the copula in relation to thought in general."[35] Through the *assertoric* function an objectively valid relationship of thoughts is judged to be actually existent.

We have gained these relational and modal functions of thought by analyzing the form of a judgment in general (the thoroughgoing objective unity of apperception in the consciousness of one's representations). This procedure is in keeping with the nature of pure general logic. "For since general logic abstracts from all content of knowledge, the sole task that remains to it is to give an analytical exposition of the form of knowledge [as expressed] in concepts, in judgments, and in inferences, and so to obtain formal rules for all employment of understanding."[36] These various logical forms of judgment are rules for combining representations in the objective unity of consciousness. We were able to distinguish them only insofar as we could see how they were associated with one another. Quite obviously the modal functions and the relational ones are intertwined (see p. 165, below).

Are there any more distinctions to be gained from our explication of a judgment in general? As far as relation and modality are concerned our functions are complete, for reasons which we shall consider later (see pp. 167–170). Of course various combinations of the modal and relational functions can be made, e.g., assertoric categorical, apodeictic

[35] *Ibid.*, B 99–100, p. 109.

[36] *Ibid.*, B 171–172, p. 177.

hypothetical, etc. In looking for other original functions, we must return to the general form of judging. We have not yet considered one of this form's necessary aspects referred to by Kant when he claims that the logical functions of judgment are the clue to the discovery of the categories of the understanding: "The same understanding, through the same operations by which in concepts, by means of analytical unity, it produced the logical form of a judgment. . . ."[37] We briefly touched on the matter of judgments when we considered the categorical function of thought (see p. 151). We must now consider this logical matter, i.e., the concepts contained in a judgment insofar as they are concepts in general (representations to which the analytic unity of consciousness belongs). In so doing we must consider how it is that the unity of a judgment characterized by modality and relation determines the internal form of the logical matter of such a judgment.

Let us consider the disjunctive judgment characterized by the modal function of necessity. It is obvious from our discussion of the disjunctive judgment (pp. 156–158) that since the given problematic judgments which function as the parts of the disjunctive one are all categorical, the problematic ones all have the same subject. Now, let us ask how it happens that "in concepts by means of analytical unity"[38] problematic judgments all having the same subject reciprocally determine one another in such a way that a true judgment necessarily results. We have seen (p. 145) that the analytic unity in the relationship of given concepts consists in the determination of their subordination relationship to one another according to their range (sphere) and content. Since the disjunction has to be a reciprocal determination of problematic judgments, the concepts P, P', P'', etc. as predicates of the same subject S cannot be subordinated to one another

[37] *Ibid.*, B 105, p. 112.

[38] *Ibid.*, B 105, p. 112. See the preceding paragraph.

according to their range. If they could be, then by means of the truth or falsity of one predicate-concept of S we could by derivation determine forthwith the truth or falsity of its other predicate-concepts; in this case the determination would not be reciprocal but unilateral.[39] Since the predicates are related coordinately (rather than serially), their relationship cannot be one of agreement (compatibility). In the disjunctive judgment the relationship is clearly one of the disagreement (opposition) of the predicate-concepts; if one of them can be asserted of the subject-concept, then the others taken together necessarily cannot be so asserted because they constitute the opposite of the one that can. This distinction is called the *quality* of a judgment; *affirmation* or *negation* are functions of a judgment in general. Since this qualitative distinction was won analytically from the form of the disjunctive judgment, it belongs to the objective unity of consciousness.

Now, let us consider how in the disjunctive judgment the community of given representations expresses itself through the relationship of opposition (one of the qualitative functions) "in concepts by means of analytical unity". In the disjunctive judgment a relationship of the parts of the sphere of the subject-concept is thought of in such a way that the sphere of each part is a complement of the sphere of the other parts, while together the spheres of each part constitute the whole sphere of the proper knowledge of the subject (see Kant's remarks above, note 33). This means that in the disjunctive judgment one thinks of a relationship between the whole sphere of a concept and the parts of that sphere. In

---

[39] Cf. *ibid.,* B 112, p. 117: ". . . we must observe that in all disjunctive judgments the sphere (that is, the multiplicity which is contained in any one judgment) is represented as a whole divided into parts (the subordinate concepts), and that since no one of them can be contained under any other, they are thought as co-ordinated with, not subordinated to, each other, and so as determining each other, not in one direction only, as in a series, but reciprocally, as in an aggregate—if one member of the division is posited, all the rest are excluded, and conversely."

Kant's example in the just mentioned note 33, he talks
on the one hand about the parts "of the sphere of the possible knowledge concerning the existence of a world in general" and on the other hand about the whole sphere of this
possible knowledge, i.e., on the one hand about the relationship of the concepts "blind chance", "inner necessity", and
(external) necessity by reference to "an external cause" and
on the other hand about the modality of existence in general
insofar as such modality touches the subject, namely, the
actuality of a world in general. The disjunctive relationship
of the parts of the sphere of the subject and the whole sphere
of the subject is thought as being actually in the logical matter, i.e., "in concepts by means of analytical unity". This
disjunctive relationship is the form in which the relationship
between the parts of the sphere of a concept and the whole
sphere of that concept is thought as referred to the objective
unity of apperception. This means that the forms of the *universal* and *particular* judgments are derived from the form
of the disjunctive judgment. In the universal judgment the
sphere of the subject is entirely included within the sphere
of the predicate, while in the particular judgment a part of
the sphere of the subject is included in the sphere of the
predicate; these are the functions of the *quantity* of a judgment. (To relate a predicate to a subject in a restricted sphere
presupposes negation. Therefore quality had to be treated
before quantity.)

The various logical forms of thought have now been
gained by analyzing the form of a judgment in general. The
question as to where the logical functions come from (see
pp. 148, 150) has now been answered.

One of the main concerns of general logic is to analyze
the synthetic unity of consciousness into its various logical
functions of judging. In the preceding sketch[40] these logical

[40] The general outlines of this sketch were suggested by K. Reich, pp. 46–55.
(See p. 150, above.)

functions have been presented in an order starting first with
the interconnections of the relational and modal ones and
then proceeding to the qualitative and quantitative ones. According to Kant, "since general logic abstracts from all content of knowledge, the sole task that remains to it is to give
an analytical exposition of the form of knowledge [as ex-
pressed] in concepts, in judgments, and in inferences, and so
to obtain formal rules for all employment of understanding."[41] In the "Paralogisms of Pure Reason" he states that the
analytical exposition (as far as the functions of judgment are
concerned) proceeds in the order, modality, relation, quality,
quantity.[42] Yet in the famous table of the logical functions
of judgment given in the *Critique of Pure Reason,* B 95, he
proceeds from quantity, to quality, to relation, to modality.
Why so? At this point in the *Critique* the table of the logical
forms of judgment serves as the clue for discovering the table
of the pure categories of the understanding. And the *Critique*
proceeds synthetically rather than analytically (progressively
from condition to conditioned rather than regressively from
conditioned to condition).[43] Accordingly, in several places in

[41] *Critique of Pure Reason,* B 171–172, p. 177.

[42] "If, on the other hand, we should proceed *analytically,* starting from the
proposition 'I think', as a proposition that already in itself includes an existence as given, and therefore modality, and analysing it in order to ascertain
its content, and so to discover whether and how this 'I' determines its existence in space or time solely through that content, then the propositions of
the rational doctrine of the soul would not begin with the concept of a thinking being in general, but with a reality, and we should infer from the manner
in which this reality is thought, after everything empirical in it has been
removed, what it is that belongs to a thinking being in general. This is shown
in the following table: 1. *I think* [modality], 2. *as subject* [relation], 3. *as
simple subject* [quality], 4. *as identical subject in every state of my thought*
[quantity]." *Ibid.,* B 418–419, pp. 375–376.

[43] Cf. "With that work complete, I offer here a sketch based on an *analytical*
method, while the *Critique* itself had to be executed in the *synthetical* style,
in order that the science may present all its articulations, as the structure of
a peculiar cognitive faculty, in their natural combination." *Prolegomena to
Any Future Metaphysics,* Mahaffy-Carus translation extensively revised by
Lewis White Beck (The Library of Liberal Arts, New York: Bobbs-Merrill, 1950),
p. 11 (Ak. 264).

the *Critique* he rearranges and modifies the usual orders of general logic to suit the purposes of transcendental logic.[44] In the latter, quantity, quality, relation, modality are the headings of the thought of an object in general in the synthetic order. It is clear from the mere concepts that, for example, the concept of the substance-accident relationship (relation) presupposes the concept of the real (quality), and further that the thought of the existence of an object (modality) presupposes a concept of what the object is, this being specified by means of the three preceding heads, quantity, quality, relation.

On the other hand, in general logic the doctrine of judgment must dissect the operation of judging into its various functions. In the preceding sketch there was an implicit claim that the analytic order (belonging as it does to the very nature of formal logic) must be followed in ordering the various functions of thought in judgment as regards their connections with one another. This means that from something determinate laid down as a basis, something else de-

[44] In the preceding sketch of the logical functions of judgment when quality and quantity were treated, no mention was made of the infinite and singular functions, though these appear in the table given in the *Critique* at B 95. But compare the following: "If, therefore, we estimate a singular judgment *(judicium singulare)*, not only according to its own inner validity, but as knowledge in general, according to its quantity in comparison with other knowledge, it is certainly different from general judgments *(judicia communia)*, and in a complete table of the moments of thought in general deserves a separate place—though not, indeed, in a logic limited to the use of judgments in reference to each other. . . . In like manner *infinite judgments* must, in transcendental logic, be distinguished from those that are *affirmative,* although in general logic they are rightly classed with them, and do not constitute a separate member of the division. General logic abstracts from all content of the predicate (even though it be negative); it enquires only whether the predicate be ascribed to the subject or opposed to it. But transcendental logic also considers what may be the worth or content of a logical affirmation that is thus made by means of a merely negative predicate, and what is thereby achieved in the way of addition to our total knowledge." *Critique of Pure Reason,* B 96–97, pp. 107–108. More will be said (pp. 171–172) about infinite and singular judgments when we come to consider the completeness of the table of logical functions.

terminate can be gained analytically. This is exactly the procedure we followed in starting first with the general form
of a judgment, whereby given concepts are so united that
they are related to original pure apperception and its necessary unity, and from this form deriving the various functions
in an analytic order from one another.

Can this list lay any claim to being complete? This, of
course, is the second question to be answered in this Part
Two (see p. 148).[45] That there are only these four heads
(modality, relation, quality, quantity) follows from the explication of a judgment in general. Let us first note that there is
a division between modality and relation on the one hand,
and quality and quantity on the other.[46] We have seen earlier
(p. 146) that the logical form of *every* judgment consists in
the original synthetic unity of apperception. This means that
representations are so united in a judgment that this judgment is objectively valid, i.e., true. This characteristic of a
judgment, which precedes all other characteristics, refers to
modality. "The *modality* of judgments is a quite peculiar
function. Its distinguishing characteristic is that it contributes

[45] In answering this question I shall follow fairly closely the solution given by
Reich in pp. 88–95 of his book. However, much of the answer in what follows
was worked out by me before my discovery of Reich's book. Warner Wick
once suggested that I use Kant's concepts of reflection, which I did in my own
work on the problem. Reich also uses the concepts of reflection; his solution
is somewhat neater than the one I succeeded in gaining.

[46] In speaking of the categories Kant remarks that "while it [table of cate-
gories] contains four classes of the concepts of understanding, it may . . . be
divided into two groups; those in the first group [quantity, quality] being
concerned with objects of intuition, pure as well as empirical, those in the
second group [relation, modality] with the existence of these objects, in their
relation either to each other or to the understanding. The categories in the
first group I would entitle the *mathematical*, those in the second group
dynamical. The former have no correlates; these are to be met with only
in the second group. This distinction must have some ground in the nature
of the understanding." *Critique of Pure Reason*, B 110, p. 116. This same division must hold for the logical forms of judgment since the categories "are
concepts of an object in general, by means of which the intuition of an
object is regarded as determined in respect of one of the logical functions of
judgment", B 128, p. 128.

nothing to the content of the judgment . . . but concerns only the value of the copula in relation to thought in general."[47] And so relation presupposes modality—we relate representations in such a way that this relationship is thought as objectively valid. Accordingly, a relationship of representations is rendered necessary by means of modality's original moment of objective validity. Relation leads to quality and quantity by means of the form of the disjunctive judgment. Can there be any more heads? The division just noted between the heads gives us the answer. Modality and relation belong fundamentally together. Since a judgment is an objectively valid (modality) relationship (relation) of concepts by means of the analytic unity of consciousness, quality and quantity follow. We have seen (p. 145) that a concept is by its very form a partial representation and as such is an analytic ground of knowledge. When modality and relation are considered with reference to concepts insofar as they are analytic grounds of knowledge, then the quality and quantity of a judgment are determined. The explication of a judgment is now complete—a judgment is an objectively valid (modality) relationship (relation) of concepts, which are partial representations (resulting in quality) and are therefore analytic grounds of knowledge (resulting in quantity). This is to say that any act of knowing involves at the very minimum (in the case of the categorical function) a combination—*relation*— of representations (concepts)—these through their analytic unity, or subordination, involving *quality* and *quantity*—in the transcendental unity of apperception. These immediate judgments of the understanding called categorical can be combined in apperception—*relation*—through the hypothetical and disjunctive functions to yield more complex immediate judgments. (These immediate judgments of understanding are to be distinguished from the mediate judgments of reason, or syllogisms.) Further, such immediate judgments

---

[47] *Ibid.*, B 99–100, p. 109.

have a special relationship to the mind that holds them—
modality. There are no other heads possible. The foregoing
explication of a general immediate judgment of understanding characterizes the primordial act of cognition—the transcendental unity of apperception.

Are the moments under the four heads complete? Kant
provides the principle for answering this question in the following terse statement:

> There are therefore three logical functions [elementary and
> not derivative] under a certain head, and hence three cate-
> gories also: two of the functions manifest the unity of con-
> sciousness as regards two opposites, but the third function
> mutually connects the consciousness again. No more kinds of
> the unity of consciousness can be thought. For there is (a) one
> consciousness which combines a manifold, (b) another con-
> sciousness which combines in an opposite way, and so (c) is
> the combination of (a) and (b).[48]

[48] *Reflections on Metaphysics*, No. 5854, to be found in Vol. XVIII, p. 370 of
the Akademie edition. Erich Adickes dates it in the 1780's. Cf. *Critique of
Aesthetic Judgement*, trans. J. C. Meredith (Oxford: Oxford University Press,
1911), p. 39 note (Ak. 197): "It has been thought somewhat suspicious that
my divisions in pure philosophy should almost always come out threefold.
But it is due to the nature of the case. If a division is to be a *priori* it must
be either analytic, according to the law of contradiction—and then it is always
twofold (quodlibet ens est aut A aut non A)—or else it is *synthetic*. If it is
to be derived in the latter case from a *priori* concepts (not, as in mathematics,
from the a *priori* intuition corresponding to the concept,) then, to meet the
requirements of synthetic unity in general, namely (1) a condition, (2) a conditioned, (3) the concept arising from the union of the conditioned with its
condition, the division must of necessity be trichotomous." Also, *Critique of
Pure Reason*, B 110–111, pp. 116–117: "Secondly, in view of the fact that
all a *priori* division of concepts must be by dichotomy, it is significant that
in each class the number of the categories is always the same, namely,
three. Further, it may be observed that the third category in each class always
arises from the combination of the second category with the first. Thus
allness or *totality* is just plurality considered as unity; *limitation* is simply
reality combined with negation; *community* is the causality of substances
reciprocally determining one another; lastly, *necessity* is just the existence
which is given through possibility itself. It must not be supposed, however,
that the third category is therefore merely a derivative, and not a primary,
concept of the pure understanding. For the combination of the first and second
concepts, in order that the third may be produced, requires a special act of
the understanding, which is not identical with that which is exercised in the

How does this principle apply to the completeness of the functions of modality? In what way are the forms of the problematic and the assertoric judgments opposed to one another? In the *Critique of Pure Reason,* B 100–101 (pp. 109–110), Kant claims that "problematic judgments are those in which affirmation or negation is taken as merely possible (optional)." The problematic judgment "is thought only as an optional judgment, which it is possible to assume. . . . The problematic proposition is therefore that which expresses only logical (which is not objective) possibility—a free choice of admitting such a proposition, and a purely optional admission of it into the understanding." In the note at B 101 (p. 110) he says, "Just as if thought were in the problematic a function of the understanding [the faculty of concepts]" and not yet a function of the faculty of judgment [*Urteilskraft*]. We have seen earlier (p. 151) that concepts are the matter of a judgment. From what Kant has just said in the note at B 101, it is clear that problematic validity provides nothing more than "matter" for judging. On the other hand, assertoric (objective) validity involves the logical "form" of a judgment in general—i.e., the assertoric judgment refers the concepts contained in it to the transcendental unity of apperception. When the assertoric validity is determined by the conditions given through the merely problematic validity, apodeictic validity results; this is to say that the apodeictic combines the other two.

Under relation how are the forms of the categorical and hypothetical judgments opposed to one another? Through the former we think an "internal" relationship of concepts, while in the latter an "external" relationship of judgments. In

---

case of the first and the second. Thus the concept of a *number* (which belongs to the category of totality) is not always possible simply upon the presence of concepts of plurality and unity (for instance, in the representation of the infinite); nor can I, by simply combining the concept of a cause and that of a substance, at once have understanding of *influence,* that is, how a substance can be the cause of something in another substance. Obviously in these cases, a separate act of the understanding is demanded; and similarly in the others."

a categorical judgment we think of the predicate-concept as itself belonging to the subject-concept. We know that the subject serves as the condition for referring the predicate to the transcendental unity of apperception (see p. 152). The predicate is internally connected with the subject for the very reason that the subject does have this function of referring the predicate to truth. The relationship between antecedent and consequence is external. We have already seen (p. 155) that the truth of both categorical judgments making up the hypothetical one must be left undetermined, and their truth must be thought of as founded on their reference to possible truth through their connection in the hypothetical one. The hypothetical function of thought externally relates (the antecedent can be false without the consequence having to be so, and the consequence can be true without the antecedent having to be so) the two categorical judgments in such a way that they together constitute one objectively valid thought. The disjunctive judgment combines the internal and the external as follows. The constituent, single problematic judgments are externally related to one another: if S is P, then S is not one of the P', P'', etc.; and if S is not P, then S is one of the P', P'', etc. But at the same time this (external) relationship of problematic judgments determines the true knowledge of S; this is to say that the disjunction itself belongs internally to the objectively valid cognition of S.

In order to prove the completeness of the functions under modality and relation, we have used the concepts of reflection called matter-form and internal-external. But we have not used these concepts to discover the functions. We take the functions as already given through our earlier derivation of them (pp. 150–162); we now apply the concepts of reflection to them in order to prove their completeness.[49] In this way

---

[49] Cf. *Critique of Pure Reason*, B 317, p. 277: "Now the relations in which concepts in a state of mind can stand to one another are those of *identity* and *difference* [quantity], of *agreement* and *opposition* [quality], of the *inner* and the *outer* [relation], and finally of the *determinable* and the *determination* (matter and form) [modality]."

we heed the injunction laid down by Kant in "The Amphiboly of the Concepts of Reflection"[50] as to the misuse of these concepts. We have used the concepts of reflection merely to learn which two functions under a head are opposites in the sense that they synthesize representations in opposite ways.

What happens when the qualitative functions and the quantitative ones are compared according to those concepts of reflection called agreement-opposition and identity-difference?[51] In an affirmative judgment, what is thought in the predicate-concept is judged as being in agreement with what is thought in the subject-concept, while in a negative one, as being in opposition. In a universal judgment, what falls under the subject-concept is judged as being identical in reference to the predicate-concept, while in a particular one, as being different. But even though the negative judgment involves an opposition of concepts, this is not to say that the opposition is an analytic opposition of the concepts as such; nor is the identity thought in the universal judgment an analytic identity of the concepts. The *form* of both judgments consists in the *synthetic* unity of apperception; according to the *content* (or matter) of the judgments there is an *analytic* opposition of concepts in the negative judgment and an *analytic* identity of concepts in the universal one (see p. 147). Regarding the completeness of the functions under the qualitative and quantitative heads, Kant claims that for general logic affirmative and negative are the only functions under quality, and universal and particular are the only ones under quantity. "Logic does not consider content, i.e., the determination of a concept [and so infinite judgments are excluded from

[50] Cf. *ibid.,* B 316–349.

[51] Cf. *ibid.,* B 317–318, p. 277: "Before constructing any objective judgment we compare the concepts to find in them *identity* (of many representations under one concept) with a view to *universal* judgments, *difference* with a view to *particular* judgments, *agreement* with a view to *affirmative* judgments, *opposition* with a view to *negative* judgments, etc."

logic], but considers only the form of the relationship: agreement or opposition."[52] Also, "according to the principle of excluded middle the sphere of one concept relative to that of another is either exclusive or inclusive."[53] As to quantity, he says that "according to quantity there are only universal and particular judgments; for the subject is either completely included in or excluded from the notion of the predicate, or else it is partially included in or excluded from the predicate."[54]

How does our foregoing principle of completeness (see p. 167) square with the qualitative and quantitative functions? We have just seen that there is an opposition between two functions under each head. In the case of both modality and relation there was a third function which combined the other two opposite functions. How is one to think of such a combination under quality and quantity? We have already seen pp. 160–162) that these heads within the confines of pure general logic are concerned with the merely analytic unity that belongs to concepts as such when they are related in the objective unity of consciousness. What does one think of when he combines affirmation and negation in a separate thought (function of the infinite judgment), and universality and particularity in a separate thought (function of the singular judgment)? The results are puzzling. How is one to think of affirmation (in the infinite judgment) when there is no possibility of employing a determinate (finite) partial representation (concept); how is one to think of universality (in the singular judgment) when there is no possibility of employing a relationship of the spheres of concepts (see p. 145)? And so within the confines of pure general logic such combinations are empty. As we have already seen (p. 164

[52] *Reflections on Logic*, No. 3063 ad fin., Vol. XVI, p. 638 of the Akademie edition. Adickes dates it toward the end of the 1770's.

[53] *Ibid.*, No. 3072, Vol. XVI, p. 641. It dates from the 1790's.

[54] *Ibid.*, No. 3084, Vol. XVI, p. 650. It dates from about 1770.

note), Kant includes the singular and infinite functions in the table given at B 95 of the *Critique;* but he does so with an eye on the completeness of the table of the categories soon to come. We shall see (pp. 173–175) that transcendental logic is concerned with the forms of knowledge in general, and such knowledge involves not only concepts but pure intuitions as well. General logic, on the other hand, abstracts from all content of knowledge.

And so within the province of pure general logic no more additions can be made to our list of the logical functions of judgment; there are no other elementary functions of thought through concepts by means of the analytical unity of consciousness. The table of the pure general logical functions of unity in judgments as given at B 95 in the *Critique* is therefore complete. At B 94 (p. 106) Kant says that the "functions of the understanding [categories] can, therefore, be discovered if we can give an exhaustive statement of the functions of unity in judgments. That this can quite easily be done will be shown in the next section." And at B 105 (p. 113) he claims that "these [logical] functions [in all possible judgments] specify the understanding completely, and yield an exhaustive inventory of its powers." But yet in the *Critique* he merely sets forth the table of judgments in the synthetic order (see pp. 163–165) with an eye on the table of categories soon to follow; he does not work out the systematics of these logical functions nor does he justify their completeness. Why not?

Under Section VII (B 24–30) of the "Introduction" of the *Critique* he distinguishes a system of pure reason from a critique of pure reason. The former "would be the sum-total of those principles according to which all modes of pure *a priori* knowledge can be acquired and actually brought into being" (B 24–25, p. 58). The latter is merely a propaedeutic to such a system of pure reason; this propaedeutic merely examines the sources and limits of pure reason. The critique is concerned only with the complete examination of that knowledge which is a priori and synthetic. "I entitle *transcendental* all knowledge which is occupied not so much with objects as with the mode of our knowledge of objects in so far as this mode of knowledge is to be possible *a priori*. A system of such concepts might be entitled transcendental philosophy" (B 25, p. 59). And "if this critique is not itself to be entitled a transcendental philosophy, it is solely because, to be a complete system, it would also have to contain an exhaustive analysis of the whole of *a priori* human knowledge" (B 27, p. 60). Such a system "is still, at this stage, too large an undertaking. For since such a science must contain, with completeness, both kinds of *a priori* knowledge, the analytic [and hence such a science must contain an exhaustive analysis of the a priori knowledge developable in pure general logic] no less than the synthetic, it is, so far as our present purpose is concerned, much too comprehensive" (B 25, p. 59). Hence for the purposes of the *Critique* it is enough merely to set forth the table of logical judgments. However, transcendental philosophy would presuppose that an exhaustive analysis of the forms of thought, i.e., the whole of logic, had first been developed from the original synthetic unity of self-consciousness; the system of transcendental philosophy could then be elaborated. "The synthetic unity of apperception is therefore that highest point, to which we must ascribe all employment of the understanding, even the whole of logic, and conformably therewith, transcendental philosophy" (B 134 note, p. 154).

III. THE CATEGORIES
OF THE UNDERSTANDING

We saw earlier when we discussed singular and infinite judgments (pp. 164 note, 171–172) that such judgments are meaningless within the confines of general logic, which is concerned with nothing but the form of our knowledge. However, transcendental logic does not abstract from all content (or matter) of our knowledge but only from all empirical content.[55] Singular and infinite judgments are important from the point of view of knowledge in general, involving as it does both concepts and intuitions. If we may anticipate just a bit, the categories of totality and limitation are based on the logical functions of thought in singular and infinite judgments, and hence these forms of judgment are quite significant for transcendental logic. For example, Kant says of the infinite judgment,

> by the proposition, 'The soul is non-mortal', I have, so far as the logical form is concerned, really made an affirmation. I locate the soul in the unlimited sphere of non-mortal beings. Since the mortal constitutes one part of the whole extension of possible beings, and the non-mortal the other, nothing more is said by my proposition than that the soul is one of the infinite number of things which remain over when I take away all that is mortal. The infinite sphere of all that is possible is thereby only so far limited that the mortal is excluded from it, and that the soul is located in the remaining part of its extension. But, even allowing for such exclusion, this extension still remains infinite, and several more parts of it may be taken away without the concept of the soul being thereby in the least increased, or determined in an affirmative man-

---

[55] Cf. *Critique of Pure Reason*, B 79–80, pp. 95–96: "General logic, as we have shown, abstracts from all content of knowledge, that is, from all relation of knowledge to the object, and considers only the logical form in the relation of any knowledge to other knowledge; that is, it treats of the form of thought in general. But since, as the Transcendental Aesthetic has shown, there are pure as well as empirical intuitions, a distinction might likewise be drawn between pure and empirical thought of objects. In that case we should have a logic in which we do not abstract from the entire content of knowledge. This other logic, which should contain solely the rules of the pure thought of an object, would exclude only those modes of knowledge which have empirical content. It would also treat of the origin of the modes in which we know objects, in so far as that origin cannot be attributed to the objects. General logic, on the other hand, has nothing to do with the origin of knowledge, but only considers representations, be they originally a *priori* in ourselves or only empirically given, according to the laws which the understanding employs when, in thinking, it relates them to one another. It deals therefore only with that form which the understanding is able to impart to the representations, from whatever source they may have arisen."

ner. These judgments, though infinite in respect of their logical extension, are thus, in respect of the content of their
knowledge, limitative only, and cannot therefore be passed
over in a transcendental table of all moments of thought in
judgments, since the function of the understanding thereby
expressed may perhaps be of importance in the field of its
pure *a priori* knowledge.[56]

And so transcendental logic is very much concerned to show
that concepts are meaningful only when they have an intuitive content.[57]

Kant says that the categories "are concepts of an object
in general, by means of which the intuition of an object is
regarded as determined in respect of one of the logical functions of judgment."[58] In Part Two we have seen that the table
of the logical forms of judgment given in the *Critique* at B 95
is complete (see pp. 165–173). In the light of a category's
characterization just cited, the table of categories given at
B 106 must be complete too. This agreement of the categories
with the logical functions is the basis for the *metaphysical
deduction* of the categories.[59] In fact this metaphysical deduction provides the complete enumeration of the twelve
categories.[60] The *transcendental deduction* shows that these

[56] *Ibid.,* B 97–98, p. 108.

[57] Cf. *ibid.,* B 102, p. 111: "Transcendental logic . . . has lying before it a
manifold of *a priori* sensibility, presented by transcendental aesthetic, as material for the concepts of pure understanding. In the absence of this material
those concepts would be without any content, therefore entirely empty." Also,
B 75, p. 93: "Thoughts without content are empty, intuitions without concepts
are blind."

[58] *Ibid.,* B 128, p. 128.

[59] Cf. *ibid.,* B 159, p. 170: "In the *metaphysical deduction* the *a priori* origin
of the categories has been proved through their complete agreement with the
general logical functions of thought. . . ."

[60] No more ultimate account of why there are just these twelve categories
is possible; they are the cognizing correlates of the logical functions of judgment, which were differentiated by analyzing the nature of judging in general.
Cf. *ibid.,* B 145–146, p. 161: "This peculiarity of our understanding, that it can
produce *a priori* unity of apperception solely by means of the categories, and
only by such and so many, is as little capable of further explanation as why
we have just these and no other functions of judgment, or why space and
time are the only forms of our possible intuition."

twelve categories can relate a priori to objects, but it contains no principle for the enumeration of the categories. The table of the logical functions of judgment provides the basis for enumerating the categories, the transcendental principles of pure understanding, the metaphysical principles of corporeal nature, and the principles contained in the *Transition from the Metaphysical Foundations of Natural Science to Physics.*

The categories are

concepts of an object in general, by means of which the intuition of an object is regarded as determined in respect of one of the logical functions of judgment. Thus the function of the categorical judgment is that of the relation of subject to predicate; for example, 'All bodies are divisible'. But as regards the merely logical employment of the understanding, it remains undetermined to which of the two concepts the function of the subject, and to which the function of predicate, is to be assigned. For we can also say, 'Something divisible is a body'. But when the concept of body is brought under the category of substance, it is thereby determined that its empirical intuition in experience must always be considered as subject and never as mere predicate. Similarly with all the other categories.[61]

The pure categories are rules according to which a manifold of intuition is synthesized to yield knowledge of an object in general. Kant refers to the categories as the pure concepts of the understanding. Since they are pure, they cannot be pictured; they are functions of thought which impose a unity on a manifold (or variety) of sensible intuition, which can be pictured.

Since the categories are a priori and are therefore not abstractions from sense perceptions, they owe their origin to

[61] *Ibid.,* B 128–129, p. 128. Cf. also *ibid.,* B 143, p. 160: "But that act of understanding by which the manifold of given representations (be they intuitions or concepts) is brought under one apperception, is the logical function of judgment. . . . All the manifold, therefore, so far as it is given in a single empirical intuition, is *determined* in respect of one of the logical functions of judgment, and is thereby brought into one consciousness. Now the *categories* are just these functions of judgment, in so far as they are employed in determination of the manifold of a given intuition."

the very nature of the mind itself. But they are not mere sub-jective conditions of thought; they have objective validity. Thought imposes upon objects certain categorical character-istics, and objects insofar as they are objects known to us must have these characteristics. Thus we can have a priori knowledge of objects in general. But yet this knowledge is limited to objects that can be given in sensible intuition; we can know a priori that all substances are permanent, but not that the soul is a substance and so immortal. *The tran-scendental deduction of the categories* is concerned with their objective validity, the extent of their employment, and the limits of their legitimate use. For the purposes of this essay there is no necessity to enter into the details of this deduction. For those interested, I might remark that Kant fleshed out this deduction far more fully than he did the metaphysical one; in fact, he provided the world with two different versions of it.

In order for the pure categories to have objective validity (and not merely subjective validity) they must be related to sensibility. The

> categories have this peculiar feature, that only in virtue of the general condition of sensibility can they possess a deter-minate meaning and relation to any object. Now when this condition has been omitted from the pure category, it can contain nothing but the logical function for bringing the mani-fold under a concept. By means of this function or form of the concept, thus taken by itself, we cannot in any way know and distinguish what object comes under it, since we have abstracted from the sensible condition through which alone objects can come under it. Consequently, the categories re-quire, in addition to the pure concept of understanding, determinations of their application to sensibility in general (schemata). Apart from such application they are not con-cepts through which an object is known and distinguished from others, but only so many modes of thinking an object for possible intuitions, and of giving it meaning, under the requisite further conditions, in conformity with some func-tion of the understanding, that is, *of defining it.* But they cannot themselves be defined. . . . The pure categories are nothing but representations of things in general, so far as

the manifold of their intuition must be thought through one or other of these logical functions. Magnitude is the determination which can be thought only through a judgment which has quantity (*judicium commune*); reality is that determination which can be thought only through an affirmative judgment; substance is that which, in relation to intuition, must be the last subject of all other determinations. But what sort of a thing it is that demands one of these functions rather than another, remains altogether undetermined. Thus the categories, apart from the condition of sensible intuition, of which they contain the synthesis, have no relation to any determinate object, cannot therefore define any object, and so do not in themselves have the validity of objective concepts.[62]

From what Kant says here one can see that the logical forms of judgment and the *pure* categories are really the same synthetic functions; yet the pure categories are potentially functions of knowing objects whenever the understanding is directed to the determination of a manifold of intuition, while the logical forms abstract completely from intuition and are both potentially and actually merely pure forms of thought of any objects whatsoever. The pure categories are empty insofar as their contents are the empty forms of thought; they refer merely to an object in general and would hence *seem* to apply even to noumena, to the extent that we can think about noumena at all.[63] From this same passage we can see that the schematized categories apply only to sensible objects.

    What, now, are the transcendental schemata? Whenever

[62] *Ibid.,* A 244–246, pp. 263–264.

[63] Cf. *ibid.,* B 309, pp. 270–271: "If I remove from empirical knowledge all thought (through categories), no knowledge of any object remains. For through mere intuition nothing at all is thought, and the fact that this affection of sensibility is in me does not [by itself] amount to a relation of such representation to any object. But if, on the other hand, I leave aside all intuition, the form of my thought still remains—that is, the mode of determining an object for the manifold of a possible intuition. The categories accordingly extend further than sensible intuition, since they think objects in general, without regard to the special mode (the sensibility) in which they may be given."

a general concept is thought to represent an object, there must be a certain homogeneity between the concept and the object.[64] Since all concepts are partial representations (see p. 145), how do they represent objects? Intuitions are immediately related to individual objects; whenever we picture to ourselves a man, we have an *image* of him as possessing some particular height, hair color, eye color, etc. But a concept abstracts from such particular qualities and thus makes possible the thought of many men at once by means of their common characteristics. A concept represents an object by means of a *schema*. When I think of a man, I generate an image according to a rule. In my imagination I delineate in a general manner the figure of a two-footed upright animal, and am not limited (as in the case of an image) to any single determinate figure. Kant defines a schema as a "representation of a universal procedure of imagination in providing an image for a concept."[65] So much for empirical concepts. In the case of pure mathematical concepts, much the same holds. To construct a triangle the rule says to draw a plane figure having three straight sides which meet at three vertices. And there are infinitely many images which can be generated in accordance with this rule.

But what about the categories? He asserts that "the schema of a *pure* concept of understanding can never be brought into any image whatsoever."[66] In other words, for the categories there are no corresponding given intuitions (images) with which these concepts are homogeneous; empirical concepts are homogeneous with empirical intuitions, and mathematical concepts with the pure sensible intuitions of time and space. At B 174 (p. 179) of the *Critique* he speaks of "the rule (or rather the universal condition of rules), which is given in the pure concept of understanding." A universal

[64] Cf. *ibid.*, B 176.

[65] *Ibid.*, B 179–180, p. 182.

[66] *Ibid.*, B 181, p. 183.

condition of rules would be a rule for rules. The category of substance is related to the concept of man as the latter in turn is related to the image of a particular man. Since the categories are rules for rules, it is impossible to give images for them. The category of causation, to cite another example, gives the rule for particular empirical concepts of causal connection, which are usually called causal laws; these empirical laws (e.g., fire burns, water cools) give the rules for connecting particular phenomena and hence can have images.

What must the schema of a category be like in order that the category may be connected with intuition? The schema must be pure, or else the connection would be empirical; and it has to be homogeneous with both the category and the intuition. It must be intellectual (i.e., a product of spontaneity) in order to be homogeneous with the category. It has to be sensible in order to be homogeneous with intuition. To be both sensible and yet pure, it must be connected with the pure form of intuition; Kant turns to time as the pure form of intuition required. Since the pure category is a concept of the pure synthetic unity of an intuitive manifold in general, the pure synthetic unity of the manifold of time must come under it. Not only does time contain in itself a manifold of pure intuition; it is also the form of inner sense and is accordingly the formal condition of the synthesis of all representations whatsoever.[67] A transcendental determination of time is homogeneous with the category since such a determination is universal and rests on an a priori rule; it is also homogeneous with appearances since time is contained in every empirical representation of an object. Therefore the transcendental determination of time is the me-

[67] Cf. *ibid.*, B 177, p. 181: "Time, as the formal condition of the manifold of inner sense, and therefore of the connection of all representations, contains an a *priori* manifold in pure intuition." Also, *ibid.*, A 99, p. 131: "All our knowledge is thus finally subject to time, the formal condition of inner sense. In it they must all be ordered, connected, and brought into relation."

diating representation which makes possible the application of the categories to appearances, and as such this determination is identified with the transcendental schema.[68]

Imagination has an intermediate position between sensibility and understanding. It is the synthesizing faculty directly related to intuitions; it represents an object in intuition even when the object is not present.[69] The synthesis of the manifold of sensible intuition under the form of time is the work of imagination. It is a figurative synthesis (*synthesis speciosa*) and is to be distinguished from the purely intellectual synthesis (*synthesis intellectualis*) of understanding.[70] But yet it is a transcendental synthesis which is a priori and is also the condition of the possibility of a priori knowledge. Since all human intuition is sensible, imagination is therefore connected with sensibility. Imagination is in the service of understanding when it synthesizes the sensible manifold in accordance with the pure concepts of understanding. This transcendental synthesis of imagination is the first working of understanding upon sensibility and is the first application of understanding to objects of human experience. The expressions "transcendental synthesis of imagination" and "transcendental synthesis of apperception" indicate two different aspects (pointing out the degree of removal of spontaneity from passive sensibility) of one and the same transcendental synthesis. "It is one and the same spontaneity, which in the one case, under the title of imagination, and in the other case, under the title of understanding, brings combination into the manifold of intuition."[71] In such synthetic activity imagination is said to be productive. (It is reproductive when its synthesis is entirely subject to empirical laws of association, and such synthesis is empirical. The reproduc-

[68] Cf. *ibid.*, B 177–178.

[69] Cf. *ibid.*, B 151.

[70] Cf. *ibid.*, B 151.

[71] *Ibid.*, B 161 note, pp. 171–172.

tive synthesis is treated in psychology rather than in transcendental philosophy.) Now, the transcendental schemata are the ways in which a given manifold of intuition is combined in one time by the transcendental synthesis of productive imagination. The transcendental schemata are, then, products of the transcendental synthesis of productive imagination.[72]

Every pure category can be characterized as the concept of the synthesis of a manifold of intuition in the cognition of some object. Every schematized category can be characterized as the concept of this synthesis in time. The synthesis involved in both is the same, but the schematized category can be applied to nothing but a manifold of intuition given through the form of time. I pointed out earlier (p. 178) that the pure categories relate only to objects in general and would seem to apply necessarily to all objects whatsoever (even to noumena). But the schematized categories contain within themselves transcendental determinations of the pure intuition of time, and so their application is limited to objects of human experience (phenomena).

Having started with the transcendental unity of apperception, we have now discerned quite a few distinguishable aspects of that original act. At this point it might be helpful briefly to make explicit what the various logical functions of judgment, pure categories, schematized categories, and transcendental schemata are.[73] We shall consider these in the synthetic order (see pp. 163–165, above).

Under the head of quantity the pure categories are derived from the logical forms of judgment "This S is P", "Some S is P", "All S is P". These pure categories of unity, plurality, totality may be described as concepts of the synthesis of the homogeneous, for in these quantitative judgments the ob-

[72] Cf. ibid., B 179–180.

[73] For this I have found very helpful H. J. Paton's Kant's Metaphysic of Experience (London: George Allen and Unwin Ltd., 1936), Vol. II, pp. 42–65.

jects referred to by the subject-concept are regarded as being homogeneous with one another. The schematized categories are concepts of the synthesis of the homogeneous in time and space; as such they are the categories of extensive quantity. The transcendental schemata which are the products of this synthesis are all number.

Under the head of quality the pure categories are derived from the logical forms of judgment "S is P", "S is not P", "S is non-P". These pure categories of reality, negation, limitation are concepts of the synthesis of being, not-being, being and not-being. The schematized categories are concepts of the synthesis of being, not-being, being and not-being in time and space; as such they are the categories of intensive quantity. The transcendental schemata which are the products of this synthesis are all degree (both of sensation and of what corresponds to sensation).

Real, experiential objects have not only quantity and quality; they also have a fixed position in one common time and space and stand in definite relations to one another. As we saw earlier (p. 176), in the merely logical categorical judgment the subject and the predicate can be interchanged; but in that pure category which is the synthesis of subject and predicate the subject is regarded as a subject which can never be a predicate. The schematized category is the concept of the synthesis of the unchanging subject to which the changing predicates belong and is usually called by Kant the category of substance and accident. Permanence is the transcendental schema which is the product of this synthesis. The second pure category of relation is the concept of the synthesis of antecedent and consequence, corresponding to the hypothetical judgment. The schematized category is the concept of this synthesis of antecedent and consequence in which the consequence succeeds the antecedent in time and is called the category of cause and effect. Necessary succession in time is the transcendental schema which is the product of this synthesis. The third pure category of relation, which corresponds to the disjunctive form of judgment, is that of community and is the concept of the synthesis of ultimate subjects according to which the predicates of one subject have their ground in another and vice versa. The schematized category is the concept of the synthesis of un-changing substances according to which the changing acci-dents of one substance have their cause in another and vice versa, and it is called the category of interaction. The tran-scendental schema which is the product of this synthesis is the necessary coexistence of the accidents of one substance with those of another.

The schematized categories of quantity and quality de-termine the intuitive manifold provided by objects, while those of relation determine objects as enduring substances and the relationships of objects to one another. The schemata of modality are not concerned with the necessary traits of objects but rather with their relation to the mind that knows them. The pure categories of possibility, actuality, and neces-sity correspond to the problematic, assertoric, and apodeictic forms of judgment. These pure categories are nothing but concepts of the synthesis which is present in every judg-ment. The pure category of possibility is the concept of that synthesis which is self-consistent according to the formal laws of thought. The schematized category is the concept of productive imagination's transcendental synthesis insofar as this synthesis involves the forms of intuition. The tran-scendental schema which is the product of this synthesis is the agreement of different representations with the condi-tions of time in general. The pure category of actuality is the concept of that synthesis which is present in every judg-ment that claims to determine a real object. The schematized category is the concept of productive imagination's tran-scendental synthesis insofar as this synthesis involves the matter of intuition given at a determinate time. Existence at a determinate time is the transcendental schema which is the product of this synthesis. The pure category of necessity is

the concept of that synthesis which is present in every judgment that follows logically from other concepts or judgments according to the formal laws of thought. The schematized category is the concept of productive imagination's
transcendental synthesis insofar as this synthesis determines
the given manifold with respect to the whole of time. Existence at all times is the transcendental schema which is the
product of this synthesis.

The schemata, then, are sensible characteristics which
must belong to all objects insofar as the sensible manifold of
these objects is combined in one time. Kant's conclusion
is that the schemata are a priori determinations of time in
accordance with rules. These rules relate (in the synthetic
order of the categories) to the time-series, the time-content,
the time-order, and the totality of time in respect of all possible objects of experience.[74]

In view of the course of thought of this essay, it scarcely
need be said that these logical functions of thought, pure
categories, schematized categories, and transcendental schemata are merely distinguishable aspects of the original synthetic unity of apperception. Any judging of objects of
possible experience is a combination of representations in
the original synthetic unity of self-consciousness. This synthesizing activity of understanding has various aspects distinguished according to the different ways the subject and the
predicate are combined in apperception, or two or more
judgments are combined in apperception, or various judgments are related to the whole knowing faculty of the mind
in apperception. In the empirical judgment "All trees have
branches", the aspects of the form of uniting the representations "trees" and "branches" in apperception which are involved are the categorical, universal, affirmative; and the
modality (depending as it does on how the judgment is held
by the mind) may be problematic, assertoric, or apodeictic.

[74] Cf. *Critique of Pure Reason*, B 184.

This judgment involves the pure categories of inherence and subsistence, totality, reality, possibility, actuality, and necessity. The schemata involved which make possible the application of these categories to the representations contained in this judgment are permanence, number, degree, the agreement of the synthesis of "trees" and "branches" with the conditions of time in general, existence at a determinate time, and existence at all times. Any other judgment (empirical or pure, analytic or synthetic) would involve all the heads, though the moments under the heads are alternatives (but one and the same judgment may involve all three of the modal moments[75]).

IV. THE TRANSCENDENTAL PRINCIPLES OF NATURE

"Transcendental philosophy has the peculiarity that besides the rule (or rather the universal condition of rules), which is given in the pure concept of understanding, it can also specify a priori the instance to which the rule is to be applied."[76] Therefore we can have a transcendental science of nature. The laws of this science, which state the ways in which phenomena must be synthesized in all experience, are called by Kant the Principles (Grundsätze) of Pure Understanding. These show how the schematized categories must apply to all objects of experience. We saw earlier (note 46) that the categories of quantity and quality go together, as do those of relation and modality. The principles likewise are

---

[75] Cf. ibid., B 101, p. 110: "Since everything is thus incorporated in the understanding step by step—inasmuch as we first judge something problematically, then maintain its truth assertorically, and finally affirm it as inseparably united with the understanding, that is, as necessary and apodeictic—we are justified in regarding these three functions of modality as so many moments of thought." I shall have more to say about modality when we come to the Postulates of Empirical Thought (see pp. 192–194, below).

[76] Ibid., B 174–175, p. 179.

divided into mathematical and dynamical.[77] The quantitative principles are called the Axioms of Intuition and the qualitative ones the Anticipations of Perception; the relational ones the Analogies of Experience and the modal ones the Postulates of Empirical Thought. The mathematical principles are concerned with the objects of intuition, while the dynamical ones are concerned with the existence of these objects in relation either to one another or to the understanding.[78]

The Axioms of Intuition tell us that the intuitions of phenomena are extensive magnitudes. To have sense perception of an object as an appearance, we must synthesize the pure and homogeneous manifold of the determinate space and time which it occupies. Therefore the synthetic unity of the pure and homogeneous manifold of the determinate space and time is one condition that must be fulfilled if we are to perceive an object. But such synthetic unity is exactly what is thought in the schematized category of extensive quantity through the schema of number. Therefore all objects as appearances must fall under this category, and this means that phenomenal objects must be extensive quantities. And hence the application of pure mathematics to objects of experience is justified.

An object is something more than the space which it occupies and the time through which it lasts. It is real insofar as it fills a determinate space and time, and as such it must have intensive quantity, or degree. Experiential objects, then, have intensive matter as well as extensive form. This matter for some object in general is that through which an object is represented as existing in space and time, and such matter is the real of sensation. Since a continuous change is

[77] Cf. *ibid.,* B 197–202.

[78] In what follows I shall briefly summarize some of the main points of Kant's discussion of these principles and shall make no attempt to detail his proofs of them. For the particulars of the *Grundsätze,* see the *Critique,* B 202–274, and Paton's *Kant's Metaphysic of Experience,* Vol. II, pp. 111–371.

possible between pure intuition and sense perception (which is empirical consciousness), there is possible a synthesis that produces a quantity (a more or less) of sensation, starting from pure intuition (complete absence of any sensation) and arriving at any particular quantity of sensation given through sense perception. Sensation thus has an intensive quantity. Since the sensible perception of objects always involves sensation(as well as intuitions of time and space), a corresponding intensive quantity must be ascribed to objects. Hence color, sound, taste, and even resistance and weight must have intensive quantity. This, briefly, is what the Anticipations of Perception tell us.

While the Axioms and Anticipations are concerned with homogeneous elements of experience which do not necessarily belong to one another, the Analogies of Experience are concerned with relations of heterogeneous elements which do necessarily belong to one another. The relations involved are those of substance and accident, cause and effect, and reciprocal causality among substances (this last combining the first two). The pure categories of relation apply to appearances through their schemata, which are determinations of time. Permanence, succession, and coexistence are the correlates of substance, causality, and community. The principles which show how the schematized relational categories apply to all phenomena are rules for all the time-relations of appearances; in accordance with these rules the existence of every appearance with regard to the unity of all time can be determined. These rules are prior to experience and give us the necessary conditions under which alone experience is possible. The unity of the time in which all phenomena exist is founded on the unity of apperception, which is manifested only in synthesizing representations according to these rules. The temporal position of objects is determined solely by their relations to one another in time; this determination is brought about by means of a priori rules that are valid for any and every time.

The First Analogy treats of the permanence of substance. Since the time with which Kant is concerned is a condition of experience, it is the one time in which all objective determinations of time have their being. All objective determinations of time (whether of succession or of simultaneity) must be constituted by referring representations to an object in which they are related; only in this way can objective relations of time be distinguished from merely subjective or from imaginary ones. Time itself is not an object. An objective time-order is constructed by setting a representation in objective time-relations to other representations. And so time itself cannot be perceived, and because of this fact experience must have a permanent object and ultimately one permanent substratum for the whole objective world of phenomena. Change (coming into existence and passing out of it) is nothing but a way in which the permanent exists; the permanent is not merely one among many appearances but is the substratum of all appearances. A change is a way of existing that follows upon another way in which the same thing exists; there is an exchange of one state of a thing for another state of that thing, but the thing itself must remain the same thing.

The Second Analogy contains Kant's famous treatment of efficient causation.[79] According to this principle all changes of phenomena take place in conformity with the law of the connection of cause and effect. The succession of appearances is nothing but a change of permanent substances. All objects that are given to us through the forms of time and space must have a characteristic according to which they can be judged by the hypothetical form of judgment. That characteristic is the schema of necessary succession in time. The pure category of antecedent and consequence receives its experiential significance when it is translated into terms of

[79] Cf. Robert Paul Wolff, *Kant's Theory of Mental Activity* (Cambridge, Mass.: Harvard University Press, 1963), p. 260: "The Second Analogy is undoubtedly one of the most powerful pieces of philosophy ever written."

time and is thereby transformed into cause and effect. Thus transformed the cause is a ground which must precede the effect (actually the cause is the ground of the existence of the effect), although a merely logical antecedent does not necessarily precede its consequence. (Compare p. 176, above, where Kant says that when the subject in a categorical judgment is subsumed under the category of substance, then subject and predicate cannot be interchanged.) What, now, is the nature of this necessary succession? We have already seen (pp. 140–142) that representations have a double nature; they may be considered simply as contents of consciousness or may be considered as representing objects. Knowledge is a connection of representations *qua* objective and not of representations *qua* subjective (see pp. 145–147, above). The only sort of relation which all representations have to one another is a time-relation inasmuch as time is the form of inner sense (see p. 180, above). Therefore representations can be arranged in a subjective time-order or in an objective one. The two orders may be quite different. In the *Critique* (at B 235–236) Kant gives the example of the parts of a house, which are perceived successively but yet objectively coexist. Hence in order to have knowledge through perceptions, we must connect them in their objective time-relations. Even a singular object is a special way of synthesizing our representations, i.e., it is not something distinct from the representations of it (an unknowable thing in itself); furthermore, the object must serve as the ground for the objective connection of our representations. So the house as an object is the synthetic reworking of the manifold of perceptions. Now, if we have a succession of objects or a succession of events, much the same sort of reworking takes place. If event A (glowing stove) precedes event B (warm room) objectively, then we must think of A as preceding B or else be wrong. It makes no difference whether we perceive A first and then B, or B first and then A in our subjective consciousness. There is no necessity in the order of our subjective consciousness, but there is necessity in our synthetic reorganization of it. We think objective succession through the schematized category of cause and effect. We saw earlier (pp. 179–180) that the categories are rules for rules. Accordingly, the universal law of efficient causation is imposed a priori by the mind upon objects, while particular causal laws can be known only a posteriori. All such empirical laws are merely particular determinations of the one universal law.[80]

The Third Analogy tells us that substances stand in a relation of reciprocal causality with respect to their accidents. This Third Analogy arises from a combination of the other two (see p. 167 and note 48), but is not derivative from them. Though we can show that substance and causality are necessary conditions of experience, we cannot conclude that substances mutually influence one another. Kant argues for such influence by pointing out that some sense perceptions can follow one another reciprocally (we can see first the moon and then the earth, or vice versa), while in the case of the Second Analogy, where one has an objective unilinear succession of perceptions, this reciprocity cannot hold. Since our representations *qua* objective are perceptions of objects (or permanent substances, which are not things in themselves), we can say that inasmuch as our perceptions of certain objects follow one another reciprocally, the objects are coexistent. This reversibility of our representations is a criterion for distinguishing objective coexistence from objective

[80] Cf. *Critique of Pure Reason,* B 165, p. 173: "Nature, considered merely as nature in general, is dependent upon these categories as the original ground of its necessary conformity to law (*natura formaliter spectata*). Pure understanding is not, however, in a position, through mere categories, to prescribe to appearances any a *priori* laws other than those which are involved in a *nature in general,* that is, in the conformity to law of all appearances in space and time. Special laws, as concerning those appearances which are empirically determined, cannot in their specific character be *derived* from the categories, although they are one and all subject to them. To obtain any knowledge whatsoever of these special laws, we must resort to experience; but it is the a *priori* laws that alone can instruct us in regard to experience in general, and as to what it is that can be known as an object of experience."

unilinear succession. Also, we can say that if the objects perceived coexist, then the succession of our representations must be reversible. Now, a sense perception is not something lying between us and the object; it is an object's state, which is immediately present to our minds. The object is made up of such possible or actual perceptions bound up in a necessary synthetic unity. If the reciprocal succession of our perceptions is grounded on coexistent objects, then the reciprocal succession of the states, or determinations, must be grounded on coexistent objects. If the objects were things in themselves, then it might be argued that their coexistence could determine the reversibility of our perceptions; but it could not be argued that the states of the two coexistent objects must therefore be reciprocally determined by the two objects. Since objects are not things in themselves, we can infer from the coexistence of objects that they must interact. And so coexistent objects must mutually determine one another's states; accordingly, we can know that the order of our representations must be reversible, and we can know that the objects coexist. The necessity involved here is imposed by a concept of the relation of substances in which one substance contains states whose ground is contained in the other; the relation is one of causal action of one substance upon another and is furthermore reciprocal. The pure category of community so schematized is that of interaction. It is the concept of functional interdependence, expressed in such equations as the laws of motion, and is of the utmost importance for science. The world as science knows it is a system of functional relations between measurable quantities.

The Postulates of Empirical Thought are concerned with the existence of objects in relation to the mind. Up till now I have shown that if an object is to be an object of experience, then it must have in itself certain necessary traits, or determinations; it must have extensive and intensive quantity, and must be a substance (with changing accidents) in causal interaction with all other such substances. The concept of the object when it is considered only in itself does not contain possibility, actuality, and necessity; these are determinations of an object in a sense different from the aforementioned ones. The Postulates add to the concept of an object nothing more than the cognitive faculty in which the concept originates and has its seat. But Kant is not concerned with merely logical possibility, actuality, and necessity; rather, he explains real possibility, actuality, and necessity by reference to experience. Possibility depends on the form of experience, actuality mainly on the matter of experience, and necessity (as is to be expected from p. 167 and note 48) on the combination of the two. The First Postulate says that if things are to be possible, then the concept of these things must agree with the forms of intuition (time and space) and with the transcendental unity of apperception. The Second Postulate states that what is connected with the material conditions of experience (viz., sensation) is actual. This means that we must have sense perception in order to have knowledge of the actuality of things. The Third Postulate says that the necessary is that whose connection with the actual is determined in accordance with the universal conditions of experience (namely, the Analogies). The necessity involved here is hypothetical (not absolute) by means of the causal law expressed in the Second Analogy. Such necessity applies only to the changing states of substances and not to the substances themselves, inasmuch as substances endure and do not come to be and pass away. If the cause is actual, then the effect must exist; if we have actual experience of the cause of something, then by thought we can affirm the necessary existence of objects.[81] These Postulates must apply to all experiential objects; accordingly, every object of experience is possible, actual, and necessary—but in different respects. An object has different relations to the mind because of

[81] Cf. *ibid.*, B 239.

the different aspects of the object which were just discussed. Every object has a form imposed by the mind, and the object is possible because of this form. Every object has a matter that is given to the mind and synthesized under that form; thereby is the object actual. Every object is a combination of form and matter, i.e., it is a substance whose accidents are causally determined; thereby is the object necessary. Accordingly, possibility is no wider than actuality, and actuality is no wider than necessity.[82]

It is not surprising that the (modal) Postulates conclude the Principles of Pure Understanding. After all, one cannot talk about the existence of an object (modality) without first having a concept of what the object is; and what it is, is specified by means of quantity, quality, relation. Throughout the Principles Kant has appealed to the possibility of experience, and so to the possibility of experiential objects. In the Analogies he argued that what is objective, or actual, can be distinguished from what is merely subjective or merely imaginary, because the actual is governed by necessity. In the Postulates he considers this possibility, actuality, and necessity. He has shown in the Axioms, Anticipations, and Analogies what objects must be if they are given to intuition and if they exist in relation to one another in a common space and time. In the Postulates he shows what relations they must have to the mind that knows them.

In view of the preceding course of thought, I scarcely need say that these various Principles are simply distinguishable aspects of the one synthesis contained in the transcendental unity of apperception (see pp. 185–186, above). The Axioms are concerned with the synthesis of the form of intuition; the Anticipations with the synthesis of the matter of intuition; the Analogies with the synthesis of the form and the matter of intuition; and the Postulates with the relations of all these syntheses to the mind that produces them. *All* the Principles apply to *each and every* object of experience.

[82] Cf. *ibid.,* B 282–285.

V. THE METAPHYSICAL PRINCIPLES OF NATURE

Part of the "General Note on the System of the Principles" in the *Critique* heralds the *Metaphysical Foundations of Natural Science:*

> . . . in order to understand the possibility of things in conformity with the categories, and so to demonstrate the *objective reality* of the latter, we need, not merely intuitions, but intuitions that are in all cases *outer intuitions.* When, for instance, we take the pure concepts of *relation,* we find, firstly, that in order to obtain something *permanent* in intuition corresponding to the concept of *substance,* and so to demonstrate the objective reality of this concept, we require an intuition in space (of matter). . . . Secondly, in order to exhibit *alteration* as the intuition corresponding to the concept of *causality,* we must take as our example motion, that is, alteration in space. . . . For alteration is combination of contradictorily opposed determinations in the existence of one and the same thing. Now how it is possible that from a given state of a thing an opposite state should follow, not only cannot be conceived by reason without an example, but is actually incomprehensible to reason without intuition. The intuition required is the intuition of the movement of a point in space. The presence of the point in different locations (as a sequence of opposite determinations) is what alone first yields to us an intuition of alteration. . . . Lastly, the possibility of the category of *community* cannot be comprehended through mere reason alone; and consequently its objective reality is only to be determined through intuition, and indeed through outer intuition in space. For how are we to think it to be possible, when several substances exist, that, from the existence of one, something (as effect) can follow in regard to the existence of the others, and *vice versa;* in other words, that because there is something in the one there must also in the others be something which is not to be understood solely from the existence of these others? For this is what is required in order that there be community; community is not conceivable as holding between things each of which, through its subsistence, stands in complete isolation. . . . [A] community of substances is utterly inconceivable as arising simply

from their existence. We can, however, render the possibility of community—of substances as appearances—perfectly comprehensible, if we represent them to ourselves in space, that is, in outer intuition. For this already contains in itself a priori formal outer relations as conditions of the possibility of the real relations of action and reaction, and therefore of the possibility of community. Similarly, it can easily be shown that the possibility of things as quantities, and therefore the objective reality of quantity, can be exhibited only in outer intuition. . . .[83]

Indeed the word "space" occurs as frequently in the Metaphysical Foundations of Natural Science as "time" does in "The Analytic of Principles" in the Critique. The former treatise is an important step in the direction of the empirical; in it are to be found instances for the extremely abstract transcendental concepts and principles of the latter.[84]

The principles of pure understanding (see Part Four above) comprise the transcendental doctrine of the objects of a pos-

---

[83] Ibid., B 291–293, pp. 254–256.

[84] In the Preface to the Metaphysical Foundations (above, Ak. 477–478) Kant says that the general doctrine of body (i.e., the Metaphysical Foundations) "facilitates the uniform progress of this science [system of general metaphysics as contained in the Critique] toward its goal, if, in all cases where the general doctrine of body is needed, one can call upon the separate system of such a doctrine without encumbering the larger system of metaphysics in general. . . . Furthermore, it is indeed very remarkable (but cannot here be thoroughly entered into) that general metaphysics in all cases where it requires instances (intuitions) in order to provide meaning for its pure concepts of the understanding must always take such instances from the general doctrine of body, i.e., from the form and principles of external intuition; and if these instances are not at hand in their entirety, it gropes, uncertain and trembling, among mere meaningless concepts. Hence there are the well-known disputes, or at least the obscurity in questions, concerning the possibility of an opposition of realities, the possibility of intensive magnitude, etc., with regard to which the understanding is taught only through instances from corporeal nature what the conditions are under which the concepts of the understanding can alone have objective reality, i.e., meaning and truth. And so a separate metaphysics of corporeal nature does excellent and indispensable service to general metaphysics, inasmuch as the former provides instances (cases in concreto) in which to realize the concepts and propositions of the latter (properly, transcendental philosophy), i.e., to give to a mere form of thought sense and meaning."

sible experience in general. The general doctrine of body takes as its subject the empirically given concept of matter and determines this concept by means of transcendental predicates already familiar to us as the categories.[85] In this general doctrine of body

> the concept of matter had to be carried out through all the four functions of the concepts of the understanding (in four chapters), in each of which a new determination of matter was added. The fundamental determination of a something that is to be an object of the external senses must be motion, for thereby only can these senses be affected. The understanding leads all other predicates which pertain to the nature of matter back to motion; thus natural science is throughout either a pure or an applied doctrine of motion. *The Metaphysical Foundations of Natural Science* may be brought, then, under four main chapters. The first may be called *Phoronomy;* and in it motion is considered as pure quantum, according to its composition, without any quality of the matter. The second may be termed *Dynamics,* and in it motion is regarded as belonging to the quality of the matter under the name of an original moving force. The third emerges under the name of *Mechanics,* and in it matter with this dynamical quality is considered as by its own motion to be in relation. The fourth is called *Phenomenology;* and in it matter's motion or rest is determined merely with reference to the mode of representation, or modality, i.e., as an appearance of the external senses.[86]

---

[85] Cf. above, Ak. 469–470: "But either it [metaphysics of nature] can treat of the laws which make possible the concept of a nature in general even without reference to any determinate object of experience, and therefore undetermined regarding the nature of this or that thing of the sense-world—and in this case it is the transcendental part of the metaphysics of nature—or it occupies itself with the special nature of this or that kind of things, of which an empirical concept is given in such a way that besides what lies in this concept, no other empirical principle is needed for cognizing the things. For example, it lays the empirical concept of a matter . . . at its foundation and searches the range of cognition of which reason is a priori capable regarding [this object]. Such a science must still be called a metaphysics of nature, namely, of corporeal . . . nature; however, it is then not a general but a special metaphysical natural science (physics . . .), in which the aforementioned transcendental principles are applied to [this] species of [sense-object]."

[86] Above, Ak. 476–477.

And so we discern a progression from the most formal to
what is less formal—from the transcendental unity of apperception with its aspects called the logical functions of judgment, to the pure categories, to the schematized categories,
to the transcendental principles of nature in general, and now
to the metaphysical principles of corporeal nature. Or one
might say that we have a progression from what is not empirical at all to what is empirical to a certain extent. Similarly,
in Kant's moral philosophy one proceeds from the categorical
imperative, which holds for all rational beings, i.e., beings
whose actions can be determined by reason rather than by
the inclinations of the senses, to the various metaphysical
imperatives, which hold for human beings, whose physical
nature and moral nature must be considered in elaborating
the system of duties contained in the *Metaphysics of Morals*.
In his theoretical philosophy he analyzes experience by considering how the form of thought synthesizes the manifold
of intuition as provided by time through inner sense in the
Critique and now especially by space through the external
senses in the *Metaphysical Foundations*.

Kant says that

the completeness of the metaphysics of corporeal nature may
be confidently expected. The reason for this is that in metaphysics the object is considered merely as it must be represented in accordance with the universal laws of thought,
while in other sciences, as it must be represented in accordance with data of intuition (pure as well as empirical). Hence
the former, inasmuch as the object must always be compared
with all the necessary laws of thought, must furnish a definite
number of cognitions, which can be fully exhausted; but the
latter, inasmuch as such sciences offer an infinite manifold of
intuitions (pure or empirical), and therefore of objects of
thought, can never attain absolute completeness but can be
extended to infinity, as in pure mathematics and the empirical
doctrine of nature.[87]

The empirical sciences are built up through observation and
experiment, and hence their working out is endless. Also,
pure mathematics is endless, since it constructs its concepts

[87] Above, Ak. 473.

in the pure intuitions of time and space, and such constructions can be infinitely many. Now, mathematics can be
applied to physical phenomena insofar as such appearances
are considered as quantities (see p. 187). Certainly its applications in empirical sciences such as astronomy are infinite.
What is the relationship between the metaphysics of nature
and mathematics? "Pure rational cognition from mere concepts is called pure philosophy, or metaphysics; on the other
hand, that pure rational cognition which is based only upon
the construction of concepts by means of the presentation
of the object in an a priori intuition is called mathematics."[88]

[88] Above, Ak. 469. Cf. also *Critique of Pure Reason*, B 741–744, pp. 577–578:
"*Philosophical* knowledge is the *knowledge gained by reason from concepts;*
mathematical knowledge is the knowledge gained by reason from the *construction* of concepts. To *construct* a concept means to exhibit *a priori* the
intuition which corresponds to the concept. For the construction of a concept
we therefore need a *non-empirical* intuition. The latter must, as intuition, be
a *single* object, and yet none the less, as the construction of a concept (a
universal representation), it must in its representation express universal validity for all possible intuitions which fall under the same concept [see this
essay, p. 179, above]. . . . Thus, philosophical knowledge considers the
particular only in the universal, mathematical knowledge the universal in the
particular, or even in the single instance, though still always *a priori* and by
means of reason. . . . The essential difference between these two kinds of
knowledge through reason consists therefore in this formal difference, and
does not depend on difference of their material or objects. Those who pro-
pose to distinguish philosophy from mathematics by saying that the former
has as its object *quality* only and the latter *quantity* only, have mistaken the
effect for the cause. The form of mathematical knowledge is the cause why it
is limited exclusively to quantities. For it is the concept of quantities only that
allows of being constructed, that is, exhibited *a priori* in intuition; whereas
qualities cannot be presented in any intuition that is not empirical. Consequently reason can obtain a knowledge of qualities only through concepts. . . .
The shape of a cone we can form for ourselves in intuition, unassisted by
any experience, according to its concept alone, but the colour of this cone must
be previously given in some experience or other. I cannot represent in intuition
the concept of a cause in general except in an example supplied by experience;
and similarly with other concepts. . . . Philosophy confines itself to universal
concepts; mathematics can achieve nothing by concepts alone but hastens
at once to intuition, in which it considers the concept *in concreto,* though
not empirically, but only in an intuition which it presents *a priori,* that is,
which it has constructed, and in which whatever follows from the universal
conditions of the construction must be universally valid of the object of the
concept thus constructed."

Now, a

> pure philosophy of nature in general, i.e., one that only in-
> vestigates what constitutes the concept of a nature in gen-
> eral [in the *Critique*], may indeed be possible without mathe-
> matics; but a pure doctrine of nature concerning determinate
> natural things (doctrine of body . . .) is possible only by means
> of mathematics. And since in every doctrine of nature only
> so much science proper is to be found as there is a priori
> cognition in it, a doctrine of nature will contain only so much
> science proper as there is applied mathematics in it.[89]

To cognize anything a priori means to know it from its
mere *possibility*, while to cognize anything a posteriori means
to know it from its *actuality* through an empirical intuition
(see pp. 192–194). The transcendental doctrine of nature, as
we have already seen (p. 196), cognizes its phenomenal objects in general from mere concepts. But the metaphysical
doctrine of body lays the concept of a determinate natural
object (matter) at its foundation. And

> the possibility of determinate natural things cannot be cog-
> nized from their mere concepts; from these concepts the
> possibility of the thought (that it does not contradict itself)
> can indeed be cognized, but not the possibility of the object
> as a natural thing, which can be given (as existing) outside
> of the thought. Therefore, in order to cognize the possibility
> of determinate natural things, and hence to cognize them a
> priori, there is further required that the intuition correspond-
> ing to the concept be given a priori, i.e., that the concept be
> constructed. Now, rational cognition through the construc-
> tion of concepts is mathematical.[90]

The expressions "determinate natural objects" and "phenomenal objects in general" do not indicate two different
kinds of things but, rather, aspects of differing degrees of
generality of the same things. If the object is a determinate
natural one rather than a phenomenal object in general, then
the intuition corresponding to the concept of the object must
be given. If this intuition is given empirically through sensation, then the *actuality* of this determinate object is known a

[89] *Metaphysical Foundations of Natural Science*, above, Ak. 470.

[90] Above, Ak. 470.

posteriori as in the empirical sciences. If this intuition is given a priori, then the *possibility* of this determinate object is known a priori as in the metaphysics of corporeal nature. And hence this metaphysics must make use of mathematics. Now,

> in order to make possible the application of mathematics to the doctrine of body, which can become natural science only by means of such application, principles of the construction of concepts that belong to the possibility of matter in general must precede. Hence a complete analysis of the concept of a matter in general must be laid at the foundation of the doctrine of body. This is the business of pure philosophy, which for this purpose makes use of no particular experiences but uses only what it finds in the separated (although in itself empirical) concept [of matter] with regard to pure intuitions in space and time (according to laws which already depend essentially on the concept of nature in general); hence such a doctrine is an actual metaphysics of corporeal nature.[91]

The *Metaphysical Foundations of Natural Science* is, then, concerned with the principles of the construction of concepts belonging to the possibility of matter in general. These principles constitute a complete system when the concept of matter is determined by the schematized categories. And so even though mathematics is used in the metaphysical doctrine of body, this use does not render this doctrine a system comprising infinitely many propositions.

The sort of construction Kant has in mind is, for example, that when two motions of one material body (considered as a mathematical point) are represented by two lines (each expressing velocity and direction) which enclose an angle, then the composite motion of the point can be represented by the diagonal (expressing velocity and direction) of the parallelogram produced by drawing lines parallel to the original two lines.[92] And so in this example we have exhibited a priori the single intuition which corresponds to the concept

[91] Above, Ak. 472.

[92] Cf. above, Ak. 492.

of such a composite motion of the point. And yet this parallelogram is a rule (or *schema*) for generating infinitely many *images* involving all manner of angles between the lines and all lengths of the lines. This single schema, inasmuch as it is the construction of a concept (a universal representation), must express in its representation universal validity for all possible intuitions which fall under the concept of such a composite motion of the point. Here we have considered the universal in the particular (see above, p. 199 note), i.e., the concept *in concreto* (though not empirically).

The transcendental doctrine of nature, on the other hand, considers only the phenomenal objects of a possible experience in general, and the knowledge involved is cognition from concepts. Accordingly, it does not need to construct its concepts of such phenomenal objects in general. Indeed it is impossible mathematically to provide an a priori intuition corresponding to a concept of such general phenomenal things. In the case of the Third Analogy of Experience (see pp. 191–192), what sort of construction is one to make for the fact that substances stand in a relation of reciprocal causality with regard to their accidents? The Third Law of Mechanics (which is the metaphysical analogue of the Third Analogy) says that in all communication of motion, action and reaction are always equal to one another; and this communication can be constructed (see above, Ak. 546). But this is not to say that the *Metaphysical Foundations of Natural Science* contains nothing but mathematical constructions. It contains also philosophical cognitions *from* concepts and even empirical examples of metaphysical concepts.[93]

Kant claims that mathematical physicists could not develop their mathematical systems of nature without meta-

[93] Cf. above, Ak. 474–476: "Under the four classes of quantity, quality, relation, and finally modality, all determinations of the universal concept of a matter in general and, therefore, everything that can be thought a priori respecting it, that can be presented in mathematical construction, or that can be given in experience as a determinate object of experience, must be capable of being brought."

physical principles, but that they nevertheless did not orga-
nize these principles in a separate system. Instead they
postulated such metaphysical laws without investigating their
a priori sources.[94] His accomplishment will be to gather these
metaphysical laws in a system called the *Metaphysical Foundations of Natural Science.*

This system indicates (among other things) which mathematical constructions are appropriate and useful for application to natural phenomena and which are inappropriate.[95]
For example (above, Ak. 518–519), a force that diffuses itself
through space so as to act on a distant body is appropriately
represented in analogy with the diffusion of the illumination
of a light through space by means of concentric spherical
surfaces that ever increase with the square of the distance
from the light source—any one of these infinitely larger
spheres is uniformly illuminated, while the degree of illumination of any one of them is inversely proportional to its
distance from the light source. On the other hand, an inappropriate mode of representation (often used) involves letting
rays diverge from a central point (the seat of the force) so that
an infinite number of concentric spherical surfaces is thereby
indicated; this is inappropriate because the rays so drawn
can never, because of their divergence, fill the space through
which they pass nor fill the spherical surface they reach. Another interesting example (above, Ak. 503–508) concerns the
infinite divisibility of matter. Since space is infinitely divisible
mathematically, the matter that fills space is likewise infinitely
divisible mathematically. But this fact does not permit one to
go on and say that since the spatial representation of matter
is infinitely divisible, matter in itself consists of infinitely
many parts. Any actual physical division of matter can never
be completed and hence can never be entirely given. Therefore, the fact that the spatial representation of matter is in-

---

[94] Cf. above, Ak. 472–473.

[95] Cf. above, Ak. 485–486, 493–495, 503–508, 518–523.

finitely divisible does not prove that matter in itself is composed of an infinite multitude of simple parts, as the atomists claim. Matter (as appearance) is potentially divisible to infinity, but matter (as thing in itself) is never actually infinitely divisible into an infinite set of simple parts.

Metaphysics is therefore an architectonic science that determines the legitimate role that mathematics may play in our natural knowledge; or, as Kant would say, the principles of the *Metaphysical Foundations* make possible a subsequent system of the mathematical principles of corporeal nature. But the task of metaphysics is not that of discovering applications of mathematics to phenomena; mathematical physics does that.[96] Metaphysics, rather, has the function of criticism.

Let us now briefly consider the system of these metaphysical principles of nature. We know (see p. 197) that the "fundamental determination of a something that is to be an object of the external senses must be motion, for thereby only can these senses be affected. The understanding leads all other predicates which pertain to the nature of matter back to motion; thus natural science is throughout either a pure or an applied doctrine of motion."

In phoronomy nothing but motion is considered. Accordingly, movability in space is the only property attributed to matter, which is then considered as a mathematical point. Motion is regarded as a quantum which is measured by velocity and direction. Only rectilinear motions are considered in phoronomy, because curvilinear ones require the addition of a cause by means of which there is a continuous change of direction; hence such motions cannot be treated merely in terms of quantity, for they need relation (cause) as well. Simple rectilinear motions can be considered as the description of a space; in this description one must pay attention not only to the space described (direction) but also to the time involved (velocity).

[96] See above, Ak. 517–518, 521–523.

> Phoronomy is, then, the pure doctrine (*mathesis*) of the quantity of motions. The determinate concept of a quantity is the concept of the production of the representation of an object through the composition of the homogenous. Now, since nothing is homogeneous with motion except motion, so phoronomy is a doctrine of the composition of the motions of the same point according to their direction and velocity, i.e., the representation of a single motion as one that comprises within itself simultaneously two or even several motions, or else the representation of two motions of the same point simultaneously insofar as they together constitute one motion (that is, they are identical with this motion), and not insofar as they produce the latter in the way that causes produce their effect.[97]

The composition of ever so many motions is reducible to the composition of two—i.e., find that motion which under given conditions is composed of two motions, then compound this with a third, and so on. But two motions of one and the same point which are simultaneously found at this same point can be differentiated in two ways. Either they occur simultaneously in one and the same line, or else in different lines comprising an angle. Those motions occurring in the former way are either contrary to one another in direction or else keep the same direction.

> Hence there are three cases. (1) Two motions (they may be of equal or unequal velocities) combined in one body in the same direction are to constitute a resultant composite motion. (2) Two motions of the same point (of equal or unequal velocity) combined in opposite directions are to constitute through their composition a third motion in the same line. (3) Two motions of a point, with equal or unequal velocities, but in different lines that comprise an angle, are considered to be compounded.[98]

These three cases are proved by letting one of the motions be represented in absolute space; the other motion is represented by a motion of the relative space in a direction that is the opposite of what this other motion would have in abso-

---

[97] Above, Ak. 489.

[98] Above, Ak. 489–490.

lute space, but the relative space moves with the same velocity as this other motion would have in absolute space.

> If anyone wants to connect the aforementioned three parts of
> the phoronomic proposition with the schema of the division
> . . . of.the concept of quantity [that is, with the categories of
> unity, plurality, totality], he will observe the following. Since
> the concept of quantity always contains the concept of the
> composition of the homogeneous, the doctrine of the com-
> position of motions is at the same time the pure doctrine of
> quantity therein. And indeed this doctrine according to all
> three moments furnished by space, namely, the unity of line
> and direction, the plurality of directions in one and the same
> line, and finally the totality of directions as well as of lines,
> according to which the motion can take place, contains the
> determination of all possible motion as quantum, although
> motion's quantity (in a movable point) consists merely in
> velocity.[99]

These phoronomic principles are the metaphysical analogues
of the Axioms of Intuition. In phoronomy motion in space is
regarded simply as an extensive magnitude.

In dynamics matter is considered as the movable insofar as
it fills a space. This dynamical explication of the concept of
matter presupposes the phoronomic one of matter as the
movable in space, but adds to matter the property of being
able to resist a motion within a certain space. Dynamical
resistance concerns the diminution of the spatial extension
of matter (compressibility). Matter dynamically resists when
the space it fills is diminished (which is quite different from
the mechanical resistance—inertia—involved when matter is
driven from its place and is thus itself moved). Matter fills a
space by means of a special moving force and not by its mere
existence. Only two moving forces can be thought of. All the
motion that one matter can impress upon another (both matters being considered as points) must be imparted in the
straight line connecting the two points. In this straight line
only two kinds of motion are possible: one by which the

[99] Above, Ak. 495.

points recede from one another, and a second by which they approach one another. The force which causes the first is called repulsive, and that which causes the second, attractive. Now, matter fills its space by the repulsive forces of all its parts, i.e., by its own force of extension, beyond which can be thought lesser or greater degrees to infinity. But if there were no other moving force to counteract this repulsive one, matter would disperse itself to infinity; all spaces would be empty, and there would be no matter at all. If matter is to exist, there must be an attractive force acting in an opposite direction to repulsion. And hence an original attraction belongs to all matter as a fundamental force appertaining to its essence.

Repulsion (or impenetrability) is immediately thought in the concept of matter, while attraction is attributed to matter by inference. By means of sensation, impenetrability provides us with the size, shape, and location of an extended thing, i.e., a determinate object in space. But attraction by itself can give us no determinate object of sensation, i.e., no matter of determinate volume and shape; attraction reveals only the endeavor of our body to approach a point outside us (the central point of the attracting body). Thus, as we have seen that there would be no matter by repulsion alone, likewise would there be none by mere attraction; for without repulsion, all matter would coalesce in a mathematical point, and space would be empty. And so the one force cannot be separated from the other in the concept of matter. Matter as that thing which fills a space in a determinate degree is possible only by means of the attractive force's limiting the repulsive one, i.e., matter is possible only by the combination of weight and original elasticity.

If this dynamical (metaphysical) concept of matter is to be mathematically constructed, then one can do so according to the law that

the original attraction of matter would act in inverse proportion to the square of the distance at all distances and the original repulsion in inverse proportion to the cube of the infinitely small distances. By such an action and reaction of both fundamental forces, matter would be possible by a determinate degree of the filling of its space. For inasmuch as the repulsion increases in greater measure upon approach of the parts than the attraction does, the limit of approach beyond which by means of the given attraction no greater is possible is determined, and hence the degree of compression that constitutes the measure of the intensive filling of space is also determined.[100]

The attractive force (weight) depends on the mass of the matter in a given space; however, the expansive (or repulsive) force (elasticity) rests on the degree to which the space is filled, and this degree can be specifically very different (as the same quantity of air in the same volume exhibits more or less elasticity according to its greater or lesser heating). This is to say that the repulsive force can with regard to one and the same attractive force be originally different in degree in different matters. And so the degree of the extension of various matters may admit of very great specific differences with regard to the same quantity of matter; conversely, the quantity of matter may as regards the same volume (i.e., its density) admit of very great differences. Hence every space can be thought of as full and yet as filled in varying measure. And specific empirical matters can be as rare as the ether or as dense as osmium.

If we review all our discussions of the metaphysical treatment of matter, we shall observe that in this treatment the following things have been taken into consideration: first, the *real* in space (otherwise called the solid) in its filling of space through repulsive force; second, that which, with regard to the first as the proper object of our external perception, is *negative,* namely, attractive force, by which, as far as may be, all space would be penetrated, i.e., the solid would be wholly abolished; third, the *limitation* of the first force by the second and the consequent perceptible determination of the degree of a filling of space. Hence we observe that the quality of matter has been completely dealt with under the

[100] Above, Ak. 521.

> moments of reality, negation, and limitation, as much as such
> a treatment belongs to a metaphysical dynamics.[101]

These dynamic principles are the metaphysical analogues of
the Anticipations of Perception. Repulsive force has degrees
and hence intensive magnitude; accordingly, repulsive force
can with regard to one and the same attractive force be originally different in degree in different matters, and so matter
in general fills space in varying measure.

In mechanics matter is regarded as the movable insofar as
it is something having a moving force. According to the dynamical explication, matter could be regarded as being at rest
as well as in motion. The moving force there considered enabled matter to fill a certain space, but this force was not
there regarded as actually causing any matter to move. Repulsion there was an original moving force potentially
capable of imparting motion. Mechanics, on the other hand,
is concerned with matters that have been set in motion, and
the force of a moving matter is regarded as present in it in
order to impart its motion to another matter (either at rest
or moving). But yet mechanics depends upon dynamics, because one matter moving in a straight line toward another
matter could impress no uniform motion on this other matter unless they both possessed original repulsive forces. Similarly, one matter could not compel another to follow it in
the straight line connecting the two unless both possessed
original attractive forces; (in mechanics Kant considers only
cases of repulsion because these differ from cases of attraction only in the line of direction of the forces). And so a
matter as moved can have no moving force except by means
of its repulsion or attraction, upon which and with which
it acts directly in its motion and thereby imparts its own motion to another matter.

We saw earlier (p. 206) that the dynamical explication of
matter as the movable insofar as it fills a space presupposes
the phoronomic one of matter as the movable in space.

[101] Above, Ak. 523.

Thus Kant builds up his definition of matter in the *synthetic order* (see above, pp. 163–165, 194) by determining the universal concept of a matter in general under quantity, quality, and now relation, all of which are merely aspects of the one objective unity of self-consciousness.

The three mechanical laws state that (1) in all changes of corporeal nature the quantity of matter taken as a whole remains the same, unincreased and undiminished, (2) every change of matter has an external cause, (3) in all communication of motion, action and reaction are always equal to one another. Quite obviously these three laws are the metaphysical analogues of the transcendental Analogies of Experience.

> The three laws of universal mechanics might . . . be . . . designated the law of the subsistence, the inertia, and the reaction of matters (*lex Subsistentiae, Inertiae et Antagonismi*), as regards all the changes of matters. That these laws, and hence all the propositions of the present science, exactly answer to the categories of substance, causality, and community, insofar as these concepts are applied to matter, requires no further discussion.[102]

In phenomenology matter is regarded as the movable insofar as it can as such be an object of experience. Here the concern is with the relations matter has to the mind that knows it. Now, the "fundamental determination of a something that is to be an object of the external senses must be motion, for thereby only can these senses be affected. The understanding leads all other predicates which pertain to the nature of matter back to motion. . . ."[103] Accordingly, the discussions in phenomenology center primarily on motion itself. We have seen (pp. 140–142) that representations can be regarded as merely the contents of our consciousness or as referring beyond themselves to the objects which they purport to represent. The representation of motion is given to us merely as an appearance, i.e., as the undetermined object of an external empirical intuition. "In order that the repre-

[102] Above, Ak. 551.

[103] Above, Ak. 476–477.

sentation of motion may become experience [i.e., objective knowledge], there is required in addition [to representation by mere sense] that something be thought through the understanding, namely, in addition to the way in which this representation of motion inheres in the subject, there is required further the determination of an object by means of this representation."[104] The movable as such becomes an object of experience when matter is determined by the predicate of motion. Motion is change of relation in space. And thus motion always has two correlates: matter and space. With regard to the appearance of motion, change can be attributed to matter just as well as to space; and either matter or space can be said to be moved. Accordingly, the first proposition of phenomenology says that the "rectilinear motion of a matter with regard to an empirical space, as distinguished from the opposite motion of this space, is a merely possible predicate. The rectilinear motion of a matter in no relation to a matter outside of itself, i.e., such rectilinear motion thought of as absolute, is impossible."[105] Clearly this "proposition determines the modality of motion with regard to phoronomy."[106]

With regard to the transformation of appearance into experience, either matter or space must be thought of as moved to the exclusion of the other. The second proposition states that the "circular motion of a matter, in contradistinction to the opposite motion of the space, is an actual predicate of matter. On the other hand, the opposite motion of a relative space, taken instead of the motion of the body, is no actual motion of the body; if this opposite motion of a relative space is held to be an actual motion of the body, then such motion is a mere illusion."[107] Does the earth rotate on its axis (according to Copernicus) or is it still while the heavens rotate

[104] Above, Ak. 554.

[105] Above, Ak. 555.

[106] Above, Ak. 556.

[107] Above, Ak. 556–557.

about it (Ptolemy)? Phoronomically (in the appearance) one cannot tell. But dynamically the actuality of the earth's rotation can be experienced. Drill a hole to the center of the earth. Drop a stone into this hole. The force of gravity acts on the stone at every distance from the earth's center, but yet the stone continuously diverges from the vertical direction (diverges from west to east) in its fall. This fact proves that the earth rotates on its axis from west to east. This second proposition "determines the modality of motion with regard to dynamics."[108]

According to the third proposition both matter and space must necessarily be represented as moved at the same time. It declares that in "every motion of a body whereby it is moving with regard to another body, an opposite and equal motion of this other body is necessary."[109] Finally, "this proposition determines the modality of motion with regard to mechanics. That these three propositions, moreover, determine the motion of matter with regard to its possibility, actuality, and necessity, and hence with regard to all three categories of modality, is obvious of itself."[110] These principles are the metaphysical analogues of the Postulates of Empirical Thought.

VI. THE TRANSITION FROM THE METAPHYSICAL PRINCIPLES OF NATURE TO THE PHYSICAL PRINCIPLES OF NATURE

In the dynamics of the *Metaphysical Foundations of Natural Science,* which was published in 1786, between the two

---

[108] Above, Ak. 557.

[109] Above, Ak. 558.

[110] Above, Ak. 558.

editions of the *Critique of Pure Reason* (1781 and 1787), Kant says:

> But one must guard against going beyond what makes the universal concept of matter in general possible and against wanting to explain a priori the particular or even specific determination and variety of matter. The concept of matter is reduced to nothing but moving forces; this could not be expected to be otherwise, because in space no activity and no change can be thought of but mere motion. But who claims to comprehend the possibility of fundamental forces? They can only be assumed, if they inevitably belong to a concept concerning which there can be proved that it is a fundamental concept not further derivable from any other (such as is the fundamental concept of the filling of space). These fundamental forces are the repulsive forces in general and the attractive forces in general (which counteract the repulsive ones). We can indeed judge well enough a priori concerning their connection and consequences; one may think of whatever relations of these forces among one another he wants to, provided he does not contradict himself. But he must not, therefore, presume to assume either of them as actual, because the authorization to set up a hypothesis irremissibly requires that the possibility of what is assumed be entirely certain. But in the case of fundamental forces, their possibility can never be comprehended. . . . [If] the material itself is transformed into fundamental forces (whose laws we are not able to determine a priori, but still less are we able to reliably indicate a manifold of such forces sufficient for explicating the specific variety of matter), then all means are wanting for the construction of this concept and for presenting as possible in intuition what we thought universally.[111]

Again,

> Besides the ether, no law whatever of attractive or of repulsive force may be risked on a priori conjectures; but everything, even universal attraction as the cause of gravity, must, together with the laws of such attraction, be concluded from data of experience. Still less will such conclusions in regard to chemical affinities be permitted to be tried otherwise than by means of experiment. For to comprehend original forces a priori according to their possibility lies generally beyond the horizon of our reason. Rather, all natural philosophy consists in the reduction of given forces apparently

[111] Above, Ak. 524–525.

diverse to a smaller number of forces and powers sufficient for the explication of the actions of the former. But this reduction continues only to fundamental forces, beyond which our reason cannot go. And thus the investigation of metaphysics behind what lies at the basis of the empirical concept of matter is useful only for the purpose of leading natural philosophy as far as possible in the investigation of the dynamical grounds of explication, because these alone admit the hope of determinate laws, and consequently of a true rational coherence of explications.[112]

From these remarks one might expect that the next step in our knowledge of nature would be empirical science—we have investigated completely the a priori forms of natural knowledge and now have come finally to the matter of knowledge, at which point we must leave philosophy and go to empirical science. But Kant conceived of a *Transition from the Metaphysical Foundations of Natural Science to Physics.*

Between 1790 and 1803 Kant was, among other things, busy working on what is now called the *Opus Postumum,* part of which is the *Transition.* At his death the *Opus* survived as a stack of handwritten pages, which were eventually gathered into thirteen fascicles (*Convolute*). The *Opus Postumum* appears in Volumes XXI and XXII of the Academy edition of Kant's works. Sections of it constitute coherent wholes, others provide illustrations, and still others are just repetitions. Erich Adickes wrote a critical exposition of it entitled *Kant's Opus Postumum,* in which he produced a coherent account of the work; this appeared as Supplementary Volume Number 50 of the *Kant-Studien* (Berlin, 1920).

In the *Metaphysical Foundations* the pure, formal structure of motion (admitting of mathematical construction) was studied. We know a priori that in general the motion of matter is caused by the fundamental forces of repulsion and attraction. We have seen (just above) that the specific variety and behavior of matter can be accounted for in no other way than by appealing to particular forces known only

[112] Above, Ak. 534.

through experience. The variety, intensity, and laws of these forces are studied by empirical physics. For Kant the ideal of a science is a system necessarily exhaustive of our cognitions of an object. This ideal is satisfied in the *Metaphysical Foundations,* where motion is treated abstractly by considering its pure spatio-temporal relations (which are constructed without any appeal to actual experience in the pure intuitive forms given by sensibility itself, and which are, accordingly, necessarily and exactly determinable by means of pure thought alone).

But the case is quite different as regards physics. How is it to effect a rational unity of the multiplicity of forces provided by empirical observation? In order for physics to become a science there must be the possibility of anticipating a priori the totality and order of these empirical forces. Actual perception (experience) cannot do the job. It merely gives us the forces without guaranteeing an exhaustive enumeration of them or a systematic form in which they are ranged. From this we conclude that either physics cannot be a science or else we must look for a way to reduce to a system the empirical forces which determine the particular nature and behavior of matter as given in experience.[113] Kant chooses the latter alternative. The matter of experience cannot be anticipated; only the form of it can be. Therefore we must set up in an a priori way the formal schematism of matter's constitutive forces, which experience reveals to us and which physics studies in their concrete realizations. Kant calls this science a physiology. It will serve as a propaedeutic for physics by preordering and prearranging the empirical search for forces in their actual realization. In the *Metaphysical Foundations,* motion *in abstracto* could be treated purely mathematically. But natural motions, dependent as effects upon causes called forces, cannot be so treated. Mathematics can serve as an instrument for calculating the quantitative

---

[113] Cf. *Opus Postumum,* Vol. XXI of the Akademie edition, pp. 161–165, 174–180, 284–294, 481–488, 524–527, 616–625, 630–645, for example.

value of the play of forces which is revealed by experience, but it cannot serve to discover the forces themselves.[114] The science mediating the *Metaphysical Foundations* and empirical physics is to be an entirely philosophical one made up of cognitions from concepts instead of through the construction of concepts (see pp. 199–202). It will point out in an a priori manner how the formal conditions of cognition serve as the clue for the discovery of all the empirical forces that physics encounters in its work.

The *Transition* is developed in two stages. In the first stage the a priori system of possible forces manifested by experience is fixed; in the second the general properties of matter are established. Finally, Kant sets up the foundation of the unity of experience and matter by the deduction of the ether; this last operation is independent of the other two.

The possibility of the realization of empirical representations (perceptions) in a subject are necessarily conditioned by the subject's forms of receptivity (time and space) and synthetic functions of thought. This means that perceptions are determined by the forms of sensibility and the synthetic functions of the understanding. If a force is to mean anything to us, it must be perceived and hence must be determined by these forms and functions. These synthetic functions are comprised in the table of the categories. By means of the categories, then, one can set up a priori the schema of all the possible forces that can affect us and be perceived by us in experience. Various sketches of this schema are to be found in the *Transition;* there is some difficulty in telling which one Kant might have settled on as being the final one. In general, the various sketches contain classifications already familiar to us—repulsive and attractive, superficial and penetrative, etc.

The formal schema of the general properties of matter is deduced in a similar fashion. Such a property is nothing but

114 Cf. *ibid.*, Vol. XXI, pp. 203–204, 209, 238–239, 241–245, 488, for example.

the dynamical behavior of a synthetic combination of forces. Every synthesis is the activity of a subject and must be conducted in accordance with the possible a priori forms of synthesis in general. The table of the categories presents us with all the possible forms. Accordingly, every empirical property that we can know anything about must conform to the categories; therefore this table provides us with a sufficient basis for setting up a priori a schema of the properties of matter. Again, there are various sketches of this schema. In general, the *quantity* of matter with regard to its moving forces concerns the ponderability of individual matter as made possible by means of an imponderable matter called the ether. Under *quality* is treated (1) fluidity and solidity, (2) drop formation and capillary action, (3) crystallization and melting. Under *relation* is treated (1) cohesion, (2) rubbing and polishing, (3) the luster of metals. *Modality* is concerned with the moving forces in a world system.

These schemata in no way replace experience. We are unable by means of them to foretell or predetermine what concrete forces or what empirical properties will affect us here and now or which ones will be given us by experience. But these schemata give us with a clue and a sure guide for exploring the empirically real; they enable us to classify in a necessary way every possible object of physics until experience gives us the actual presence of some one of these forces or properties.

The third part of the *Transition* treats of the ether. In the *Metaphysical Foundations* (Ak. 534), Kant thought that one might be justified in assuming the existence of the ether as a more acceptable alternative to the hypothesis (which he found unacceptable) of impenetrable atoms and absolutely empty space. But in the *Transition* he was not quite so cautious. He thought that the unity of physics was not sufficiently guaranteed by the a priori possibility of a manifold of forces and properties of matter. In the ether he found a unitary element coextensive with both the unity of matter and the unity of experience. The theory of the ether, whose existence is treated in Convolute X, XI, and XII of the *Opus*, figures in all the inquiries of the *Transition*. It is a matter that occupies absolutely every part of space, that penetrates the whole material domain, that is identical in all its parts, and that is endowed with a spontaneous and perpetual motion. He bases his proof of its existence upon the unity of experience. The form of all experience is space, which is unitary; hence experience is unitary. Experience is a system made up of a manifold of perceptions synthesized by the understanding in space. The source of these perceptions lies in the actions of the material forces which fill space. Accordingly, the forces of matter must collectively be capable of constituting a system in order to conform to the unity of possible experience. Such a system is possible only if one admits as the foundation of these forces the existence of an ether having the properties listed above. Therefore, the existence of the ether is the a priori condition of the system of experience.

The *Transition* as it has come down to us is merely a series of sketches for a work that was never finished. Accordingly, it suggests about as many unanswered questions as it provides solutions. I have discussed it only to indicate the place it occupies in Kant's system of corporeal nature.

CONCLUSION

Our exploration of the architectonic constituting the very core of Kant's philosophy of corporeal nature is now at an end. Kant himself did not always make clear the workings of this architectonic. My hope is that this essay, to some extent, succeeds in clarifying them.

JAMES ELLINGTON

GERMAN-ENGLISH APPENDIX OF TERMS USED IN THE *METAPHYSICAL FOUNDATIONS OF NATURAL SCIENCE*

A

Äther ether
Akzeleration acceleration
Allheit totality
Anschauung intuition
Anziehung attraction
Anziehungskraft force of attraction
Apperzeption apperception
Atom atom
Auflösung solution
Ausdehnung extension

B

Bebung trembling
Begriff concept
Berührung contact
Beschaffenheit quality, characteristic
Beschleunigung acceleration
Bestrebung endeavor
Beweglichkeit movability
Bewegung motion
Bewußtsein consciousness

C

Chemie chemistry

Construction, mathematische construction, mathematical

D

Denken thought
Dichtigkeit density
Ding an sich thing in itself
Druck pressure
durchdringen penetrate
Durchdringung penetration
Dynamik dynamics

E

Eigenschaft property
eindringen penetrate into, intrude
eindrücken impress
Einfache, das simple
Einheit unity
Elastizität elasticity
Empfindung sensation
entfernen withdraw
Erfahrung experience
Erscheinung appearance
Erzeugung production

F

fest solid

flüssig fluid

G

Gärung fermentation
Gegenwirkung reaction
Gemeinschaft community
Geschwindigkeit velocity
Gestalt shape
gleichartig homogeneous
gleichförmig uniform
Größe quantity
Grundsatz principle

H

Hydrodynamik hydro-
                    dynamics
Hydrostatik hydrostatics
Hylozoismus hylozoism
Hypothese hypothesis

I

Intussuszeption intussuscep-
                        tion

K

Kategorie category
Kausalität causality
Klebrigkeit viscosity
Kongruenz congruence
Körper body
Kraft force

L

Leben life

Leblosigkeit lifelessness
Leere, das void
Logik logic

M

Masse mass
Materie matter
Mathematik mathematics
Mechanik mechanics
Metaphysik metaphysics
Modalität modality
Möglichkeit possibility
Monade monad
Monadologie monadology

N

Natur nature
Naturwissenschaft natural
                          science
Negation negation

O

Ort place

P

Phänomenologie phenom-
                        enology
Phoronomie phoronomy
Physik physics
Punkt point

Q

Qualität quality

R

Raum space
Raumesinhalt volume
Reibung friction
Richtung direction
Ruhe rest

S

Scheidung analysis
Schein illusion
Schwere weight
Seele soul
Sollizitation solicitation
spröde brittle
starr rigid
Stetigkeit continuity
Stoff material
Stoß impact
Substanz substance

T

Teilbarkeit divisibility
Teilung division
Trägheit inertia
Trennung separation

U

Undurchdringlichkeit
  impenetrability
Unteilbarkeit indivisibility
Ursache cause
Urteil judgment

V

Veränderung change,
              alteration
Vernunft reason
Verschiebung displacement
Verstand understanding
Vielheit plurality
Voraussetzung assumption

W

Wärme heat
Wahrnehmung perception
Wechselwirkung reciprocal
                action
Wesen essence
Widerstand resistance
Wirklichkeit actuality
Wirkung action, effect
Wirkung in der Ferne
  action at a distance
Wissenschaft science

Z

Zeit time
Zitterung vibration
Zug traction
Zurückstoßung repulsion
Zurückstoßungskraft
  force of repulsion
zurücktreiben repel
Zusammendrückung
  compression
Zusammenhang cohesion
Zusammensetzung
  composition

INDEX*

* The subentries in this index are listed in a decreasing order going from the general to the particular.